Connected  Mathematics™

Moving Straight Ahead

Linear Relationships

Teacher's Guide

Glenda Lappan

James T. Fey

William M. Fitzgerald

Susan N. Friel

Elizabeth Difanis Phillips

Prentice
Hall

Glenview, Illinois
Needham, Massachusetts
Upper Saddle River, New Jersey

Connected Mathematics™ was developed at Michigan State University with financial support from the Michigan State University Office of the Provost, Computing and Technology, and the College of Natural Science.

This material is based upon work supported by the National Science Foundation under Grant No. MDR 9150217.

This project was supported, in part, by the

National Science Foundation

Opinions expressed are those of the authors and not necessarily those of the Foundation

The Michigan State University authors and administration have agreed that all MSU royalties arising from this publication will be devoted to purposes supported by the Department of Mathematics and the MSU Mathematics Education Enrichment Fund.

Photo Acknowledgements: 8 © Gary S. Settles/Photo Researchers, Inc.; 15 © Alan Carey/The Image Works; 18 © Thelma Shumsky/The Image Works; 19 © Bob Daemmrich/The Image Works; 29 © Bob Martin/Allsport; 51 © Peter Southwick/Stock, Boston; 60 © Jack Dermid/Photo Researchers, Inc.; 65 © Daniel Wray/The Image Works; 75 © Zigy Kaluzny/Tony Stone Images; 82 Special Collections, California Academy of Sciences; 88 © G. Goodwin/Superstock, Inc.

Prentice Hall

ISBN 0-13-053104-9

1 2 3 4 5 6 7 8 9 10   05 04 03 02 01

The Connected Mathematics Project Staff

Project Directors

James T. Fey
University of Maryland

William M. Fitzgerald
Michigan State University

Susan N. Friel
University of North Carolina at Chapel Hill

Glenda Lappan
Michigan State University

Elizabeth Difanis Phillips
Michigan State University

Project Manager

Kathy Burgis
Michigan State University

Technical Coordinator

Judith Martus Miller
Michigan State University

Collaborating Teachers/Writers

Mary K. Bouck
Portland, Michigan

Jacqueline Stewart
Okemos, Michigan

Curriculum Development Consultants

David Ben-Chaim
Weizmann Institute

Alex Friedlander
Weizmann Institute

Eleanor Geiger
University of Maryland

Jane Mitchell
University of North Carolina at Chapel Hill

Anthony D. Rickard
Alma College

Evaluation Team

Mark Hoover
Michigan State University

Diane V. Lambdin
Indiana University

Sandra K. Wilcox
Michigan State University

Judith S. Zawojewski
National-Louis University

Graduate Assistants

Scott J. Baldridge
Michigan State University

Angie S. Eshelman
Michigan State University

M. Faaiz Gierdien
Michigan State University

Jane M. Keiser
Indiana University

Angela S. Krebs
Michigan State University

James M. Larson
Michigan State University

Ronald Preston
Indiana University

Tat Ming Sze
Michigan State University

Sarah Theule-Lubienski
Michigan State University

Jeffrey J. Wanko
Michigan State University

Field Test Production Team

Katherine Oesterle
Michigan State University

Stacey L. Otto
University of North Carolina at Chapel Hill

Teacher/Assessment Team

Kathy Booth
Waverly, Michigan

Anita Clark
Marshall, Michigan

Julie Faulkner
Traverse City, Michigan

Theodore Gardella
Bloomfield Hills, Michigan

Yvonne Grant
Portland, Michigan

Linda R. Lobue
Vista, California

Suzanne McGrath
Chula Vista, California

Nancy McIntyre
Troy, Michigan

Mary Beth Schmitt
Traverse City, Michigan

Linda Walker
Tallahassee, Florida

Software Developer

Richard Burgis
East Lansing, Michigan

Development Center Directors

Nicholas Branca
San Diego State University

Dianne Briars
Pittsburgh Public Schools

Frances R. Curcio
New York University

Perry Lanier
Michigan State University

J. Michael Shaughnessy
Portland State University

Charles Vonder Embse
Central Michigan University

Field Test Coordinators

Michelle Bohan
Queens, New York

Melanie Branca
San Diego, California

Alecia Devantier
Shepherd, Michigan

Jenny Jorgensen
Flint, Michigan

Sandra Kralovec
Portland, Oregon

Sonia Marsalis
Flint, Michigan

William Schaeffer
Pittsburgh, Pennsylvania

Karma Vince
Toledo, Ohio

Virginia Wolf
Pittsburgh, Pennsylvania

Shirel Yaloz
Queens, New York

Student Assistants

Laura Hammond
David Roche
Courtney Stoner
Jovan Trpovski
Julie Valicenti
Michigan State University

Patricia Wagner
Holmes Middle School

Greg Williams
Gundry Elementary School

Lansing

Susan Bissonette
Waverly Middle School

Kathy Booth
Waverly East Intermediate School

Carole Campbell
Waverly East Intermediate School

Gary Gillespie
Waverly East Intermediate School

Denise Kehren
Waverly Middle School

Virginia Larson
Waverly East Intermediate School

Kelly Martin
Waverly Middle School

Laurie Metevier
Waverly East Intermediate School

Craig Paksi
Waverly East Intermediate School

Tony Pecoraro
Waverly Middle School

Helene Rewa
Waverly East Intermediate School

Arnold Stiefel
Waverly Middle School

Portland

Bill Carlton
Portland Middle School

Kathy Dole
Portland Middle School

Debby Flate
Portland Middle School

Yvonne Grant
Portland Middle School

Terry Keusch
Portland Middle School

John Manzini
Portland Middle School

Mary Parker
Portland Middle School

Scott Sandborn
Portland Middle School

Shepherd

Steve Brant
Shepherd Middle School

Marty Brock
Shepherd Middle School

Cathy Church
Shepherd Middle School

Ginny Crandall
Shepherd Middle School

Craig Ericksen
Shepherd Middle School

Natalie Hackney
Shepherd Middle School

Bill Hamilton
Shepherd Middle School

Julie Salisbury
Shepherd Middle School

Sturgis

Sandra Allen
Eastwood Elementary School

Margaret Baker
Eastwood Elementary School

Steven Baker
Eastwood Elementary School

Keith Barnes
Sturgis Middle School

Wilodean Beckwith
Eastwood Elementary School

Darcy Bird
Eastwood Elementary School

Bill Dickey
Sturgis Middle School

Ellen Eisele
Sturgis Middle School

James Hoelscher
Sturgis Middle School

Richard Nolan
Sturgis Middle School

J. Hunter Raiford
Sturgis Middle School

Cindy Sprowl
Eastwood Elementary School

Leslie Stewart
Eastwood Elementary School

Connie Sutton
Eastwood Elementary School

Traverse City

Maureen Bauer
Interlochen Elementary School

Ivanka Berskshire
East Junior High School

Sarah Boehm
Courtade Elementary School

Marilyn Conklin
Interlochen Elementary School

Nancy Crandall
Blair Elementary School

Fran Cullen
Courtade Elementary School

Eric Dreier
Old Mission Elementary School

Lisa Dzierwa
Cherry Knoll Elementary School

Ray Fouch
West Junior High School

Ed Hargis
Willow Hill Elementary School

Richard Henry
West Junior High School

Dessie Hughes
Cherry Knoll Elementary School

Ruthanne Kladder
Oak Park Elementary School

Bonnie Knapp
West Junior High School

Sue Laisure
Sabin Elementary School

Stan Malaski
Oak Park Elementary School

Jody Meyers
Sabin Elementary School

Marsha Myles
East Junior High School

Mary Beth O'Neil
Traverse Heights Elementary School

Jan Palkowski
East Junior High School

Karen Richardson
Old Mission Elementary School

Kristin Sak
Bertha Vos Elementary School

Mary Beth Schmitt
East Junior High School

Mike Schrotenboer
Norris Elementary School

Gail Smith
Willow Hill Elementary School

Karrie Tufts
Eastern Elementary School

Mike Wilson
East Junior High School

Tom Wilson
West Junior High School

Minnesota

Minneapolis

Betsy Ford
Northeast Middle School

New York

East Elmhurst

Allison Clark
Louis Armstrong Middle School

Dorothy Hershey
Louis Armstrong Middle School

J. Lewis McNeece
Louis Armstrong Middle School

Rossana Perez
Louis Armstrong Middle School

Merna Porter
Louis Armstrong Middle School

Marie Turini
Louis Armstrong Middle School

North Carolina

Durham

Everly Broadway
Durham Public Schools

Thomas Carson
Duke School for Children

Mary Hebrank
Duke School for Children

Bill O'Connor
Duke School for Children

Ruth Pershing
Duke School for Children

Peter Reichert
Duke School for Children

Elizabeth City

Rita Banks
Elizabeth City Middle School

Beth Chaundry
Elizabeth City Middle School

Amy Cuthbertson
Elizabeth City Middle School

Deni Dennison
Elizabeth City Middle School

Jean Gray
Elizabeth City Middle School

John McMenamin
Elizabeth City Middle School

Nicollette Nixon
Elizabeth City Middle School

Malinda Norfleet
Elizabeth City Middle School

Joyce O'Neal
Elizabeth City Middle School

Clevie Sawyer
Elizabeth City Middle School

Juanita Shannon
Elizabeth City Middle School

Terry Thorne
Elizabeth City Middle School

Rebecca Wardour
Elizabeth City Middle School

Leora Winslow
Elizabeth City Middle School

Franklinton

Susan Haywood
Franklinton Elementary School

Clyde Melton
Franklinton Elementary School

Louisburg

Lisa Anderson
Terrell Lane Middle School

Jackie Frazier
Terrell Lane Middle School

Pam Harris
Terrell Lane Middle School

Ohio

Toledo

Bonnie Bias
Hawkins Elementary School

Marsha Jackish
Hawkins Elementary School

Lee Jagodzinski
DeVeaux Junior High School

Norma J. King
Old Orchard Elementary School

Margaret McCready
Old Orchard Elementary School

Carmella Morton
DeVeaux Junior High School

Karen C. Rohrs
Hawkins Elementary School

Marie Sahloff
DeVeaux Junior High School

L. Michael Vince
McTigue Junior High School

Brenda D. Watkins
Old Orchard Elementary School

Oregon

Canby

Sandra Kralovec
Ackerman Middle School

Portland

Roberta Cohen
Catlin Gabel School

David Ellenberg
Catlin Gabel School

Sara Normington
Catlin Gabel School

Karen Scholte-Arce
Catlin Gabel School

West Linn

Marge Burack
Wood Middle School

Tracy Wygant
Athey Creek Middle School

Pennsylvania

Pittsburgh

Sheryl Adams
Reizenstein Middle School

Sue Barie
Frick International Studies Academy

Suzie Berry
Frick International Studies Academy

Richard Delgrosso
Frick International Studies Academy

Janet Falkowski
Frick International Studies Academy

Joanne George
Reizenstein Middle School

Harriet Hopper
Reizenstein Middle School

Chuck Jessen
Reizenstein Middle School

Ken Labuskes
Reizenstein Middle School

Barbara Lewis
Reizenstein Middle School

Sharon Mihalich
Reizenstein Middle School

Marianne O'Connor
Frick International Studies Academy

Mark Sammartino
Reizenstein Middle School

Washington

Seattle

Chris Johnson
University Preparatory Academy

Rick Purn
University Preparatory Academy

Contents

One of the most important ideas in the study of algebra is the relationship between two variables and how one can be used to predict values of the other. We often say that the value of y *depends* on the value of x, so we call the x variable the independent variable and the y variable the dependent variable. The concept of rate—how one variable changes with respect to another—is central to representing the relationship between variables and predicting pairs of values that fit the relationship.

In *Moving Straight Ahead,* students study linear functions and relationships. A *linear relationship* is one in which there is a constant rate of change between the two variables; the change in y that is associated with a particular change in x will remain the same over the range of the function. If x is increased from 2 to 4 and the corresponding change in y is an increase of 5, then y will increase 5 for each increase of 2 in x no matter what the starting value of x. The graph of such a function is a straight line. In all other functions, the rate of change is not constant but, in many cases, it is predictable. (In later Connected Mathematics™ units, students will investigate exponential and polynomial functions and the patterns in their rates of change.)

Linear relationships are probably the most important and basic of the families of functions that students will study in algebra. Straight lines, or linear relationships, are used in a variety of situations—for example, to model data, to approximate functions, and to find the rate of change on a curve.

In the *Variables and Patterns* unit, students were introduced to the idea of quantitative variables. They studied patterns of change, identified variables, and found relationships between variables. They described the relationships they found in the patterns verbally, in tables, in graphs, and then (to a small degree) with symbols. The effect of a change in one variable on the other variable was noted in tables, graphs, and equations. Students became aware of the advantages and disadvantages of each representation for describing relationships among variables and reasoning about patterns of change. They did some work finding solutions and specific information from tables and graphs. They made graphs, which required determining the range of the values of the variables and appropriate scales for the axes. Some of the patterns students studied were not easily translated into symbols; thus, students used tables or graphs to help them to reason about the relationship between the variables. Most of the relationships they generalized into symbols were linear; for example, *distance = rate × time* and *cost to rent bikes = charge per bike × number of bikes.*

Moving Straight Ahead builds on the idea of rate of change that was introduced in the *Variables and Patterns* unit. Students begin by making conjectures about what relationship between two variables is characteristic of straight lines. Then, they investigate different rates that can be represented with the general equation $y = mx$. Students discover that the rate at which y is changing relative to x is the coefficient of x. For example, the rate at which a person walks tells how distance is changing relative to time. The rate of change is the *slope* of the line that represents the relationship.

Learning to recognize a linear situation from its context, a table, a graph, or an equation is at the heart of this unit. At the same time, students continue to strengthen their understanding of the connections among these representations: How is a point on a graph related to a table, an equation, or the context? How does a solution to an equation relate to a graph, a table, or the context? The idea of the range of each variable becomes more important as students continue to use tables and graphs to find information about a situation from an appropriate viewing window on the graphing calculator.

Students explore the concept of the y-intercept in several contexts (such as the head start given to a participant in a race or the initial cost for renting a number of items). They investigate the general form of a linear equation, $y = mx + b$. The y-intercept, b, and the slope, m, are key ideas in determining the equation of a line.

Previous to this unit, students have used tables, graphs, and reasoning about the context of a problem to find information. In this unit, they are introduced to another method of finding information: solving an equation for a specific variable. Only equations of the form $y = mx + b$ are solved in this unit. In the grade 8 *Say It with Symbols* unit, other forms of linear equations are solved symbolically.

Finally, students learn how to determine the slope of a line given any two points on the line. With the slope and y-intercept, they can find an equation for a linear situation. The y-intercept is found by reasoning from the rate in a table or from a graph. More sophisticated methods for finding the y-intercept and an equation of line are developed in the *Thinking with Mathematical Models* unit.

In this unit, students investigate linear relationships. A relationship is linear if there is a constant rate of change between the two variables. That is, for each unit change in *x*, there is a constant change in *y*. The mathematics embedded in this unit are illustrated through the use of many real-world contexts. Several representative examples are used below.

Developing the Concept of a Constant Rate or Slope

Example 1   If a car is driven at 50 miles per hour, the distance it travels can be represented by the equation distance = $50 \times$ time or $d = 50t$, where *d* is the distance in miles after *t* hours.

Such a constant rate of change can be observed as a pattern in a table. As *t* increases from 0 to 1 hours, *d* increases from 0 to 50 miles. As *t* increases from 1 to 2 hours, *d* increases another 50 miles to 100 miles.

Time (hours)	Distance (miles)
0	0
1	50
2	100
3	150
4	200

In the symbolic representation, $d = 50t$, the constant rate of change shows up as the coefficient of *t*.

If we graph the data, the resulting straight line indicates a constant rate of change.

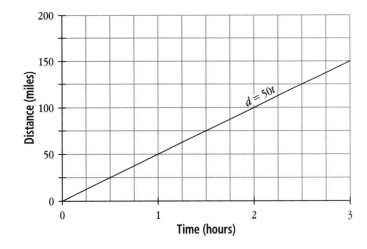

For a rate of change of 60 miles per hour, the line would have a steeper incline, and the constant rate of change would be 60. The equation of this line is $d = 60t$.

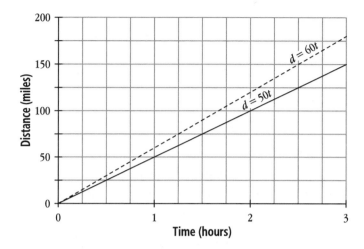

This constant rate of change is called the *slope of the line.* Slope is the ratio of the vertical change to the horizontal change. In the *Comparing and Scaling* unit, all of the situations that were studied had a constant rate of change.

To help strengthen students' understanding of linear situations, they will periodically look at nonlinear situations, usually represented in tables or graphs.

Example 2 Which of the following patterns represents a linear relationship?

x	y
$^-2$	3
$^-1$	3
0	3
1	3
2	3
3	3

x	y
$^-3$	10
$^-2$	7
$^-1$	4
0	1
1	$^-2$
2	$^-5$

x	y
$^-2$	4
$^-1$	1
0	0
1	1
2	4
3	9

The pattern in the first table is linear: the constant rate of change in y is 0, and the equation is $y = 3$. The second pattern is also linear: the constant rate of change in y is $^-3$, and the equation is $y = ^-3x + 1$. The third pattern is not linear: as x increases 1 unit, there is not a constant rate of change in y; this pattern can be represented as $y = x^2$. Such patterns of change are studied in a later Connected Mathematics unit.

Graphing calculators are used to display graphs of equations, and graphs can be used to describe patterns in a linear relationship. For example, we can see whether the line is increasing, decreasing, or neither, and we can find y given x or vice versa. The graphing calculator is also used to explore families of lines or the effect of changing the slope or the y-intercept. Students can deepen their understanding of constant rates by investigating problems such as the following on a graphing calculator.

Example 3 Investigate equations of the form $y = mx$. Substitute values for m, and graph each equation. What can you say about the slope m?

From this exercise, several patterns can be seen:

- All the lines pass through the origin (have a y-intercept of 0).
- If m is positive, the line increases from left to right.
- The greater the slope, the steeper the line.
- If m is negative, the line decreases from left to right.
- If m is 0, the line is horizontal.

Developing the Concept of the y-Intercept

Students also work through examples to help develop their understanding of the meaning of the y-intercept. In the next example, the concept of the slope is revisited in a context that introduces the y-intercept.

Example 4 Suppose the cost to rent bikes is \$150 plus \$10 per bike. Symbolically, we can represent this as $C = 150 + 10n$, where C is the cost in dollars and n is the number of bikes.

As there is a constant rate being charged for the bikes, there will be a linear pattern in the relationship between cost and number of bikes. The constant rate of change is \$10. We can create a table and a graph for this relationship.

n	C
0	150
1	160
2	170
3	180
4	190

As n increases from 0 to 1, C increases by 10; as n increases from 1 to 2, C increases by 10 again. The graph of the data is a straight line.

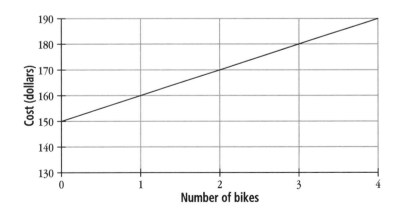

The slope of the line is 10. Also, notice that the line does not pass through the origin. It crosses the y-axis (the vertical axis) at \$150. This point is called the *y-intercept*. For 0 bikes, the cost is \$150: there is a fixed charge in addition to the charge per bike. The y-intercept is the constant term in the related equation, $C = 150 + 10n$.

Students' use of graphing calculators will help them strengthen their understanding of the y-intercept, as in the following activity.

Example 5 Investigate lines of the form $y = x + b$. Substitute values for b into the equation, and graph each line.

From this exercise, these things can be seen:

- The lines are all parallel to each other, and they all have a slope of 1.
- The lines are parallel to the line $y = x$. If b is positive, the line $y = x$ moves b units up; if b is negative, the line $y = x$ moves b units down.

Solving an Equation

All three representations—symbolic expressions, tables, and graphs—can be helpful in solving equations. For instance, in example 4 above, we might want to know the cost to rent 75 bikes or to know how many bikes we can rent for \$300. In either case, we are solving for one of the variables. We can find this information in several ways:

- We can read the information from the table or graph.
- We can reason about the situation verbally: "If it costs \$10 per bike, 75 bikes will cost \$750 plus the fixed fee of \$150 for a total of \$900."
- We can solve the equation by manipulating the symbols, as done in the next example.

Example 6 In example 4, the equation for the cost to rent bikes was $C = 150 + 10n$. If the cost is \$750, how many bikes were rented?

Students might initially solve this by using a table or graph or by reasoning backward: "First I must subtract the \$150 from the cost, which leaves \$600. Next I divide by 10 to find the number of bikes, which is $600 \div 10 = 60$." This reasoning leads to a "balancing the equation" method for solving an equation:

$$750 = 150 + 10n$$
$$750 - 150 = 150 - 150 + 10n$$
$$600 = 10n$$
$$\frac{600}{10} = \frac{10n}{10}$$
$$60 = n$$

Finding the Equation of a Line Given the Slope and *y*-Intercept

In this unit, students investigate only linear equations of the form $y = mx + b$. The slope of the line is m, and the y-intercept is b. Linear situations are represented in words, tables, graphs, and symbols. We can find a symbolic representation in two ways:

- We can translate the verbal situation directly into symbols, as was done in example 4.
- We can find the slope and the y-intercept and substitute them into $y = mx + b$.

Finding the Slope of a Line Given Two Points

To find the slope of a line, we need to find the constant rate of change. This rate can be found in various ways:

- The rate can be found directly from the verbal situation (see examples 1 and 4).
- The rate can be read from a table by noting the constant difference (see example 2).
- The rate can be determined by finding the ratio of vertical change to horizontal change between two points on a line (see example 7).

Example 7   The points (1, 4) and (3, 10) lie on a line.

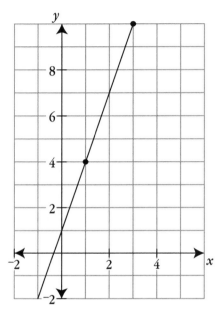

The slope is the rate $\frac{\text{vertical change}}{\text{horizontal change}}$, or $\frac{10 - 4}{3 - 1} = \frac{6}{2} = 3$.

Finding the *y*-Intercept

The *y*-intercept can be found in various ways:

- The *y*-intercept can be obtained from the verbal situation (see example 4).
- The *y*-intercept can be read from a graph or table. It is the point (0, *b*).
- The *y*-intercept can be found by substituting the slope and one of the points into the equation $y = mx + b$ and solving for *b*; see example 8. (This method is only briefly explored in this unit. It is considered in more depth in the *Thinking with Mathematical Models* unit.)

Example 8   To find the *y*-intercept for the line in example 7, substitute the slope into the equation $y = mx + b$ to obtain $y = 3x + b$. Since both points lie on the line, the *x* and *y* values of the points satisfy the equation. Substituting (1, 4) gives $4 = 3(1) + b$. Solving for *b* gives $b = 1$. We now substitute for *b* to obtain the equation of the line going through the two points: $y = 3x + 1$.

Mathematical and Problem-Solving Goals

Moving Straight Ahead was created to help students

- Further develop their understanding of variables and patterns (continuing the exploration of the ideas presented in the *Variables and Patterns* unit)

- Recognize and represent the relationships among variables in a variety of ways, including the use of words, tables, graphs, and symbols

- Identify variables and determine an appropriate range of values for independent and dependent variables

- Collect data and use patterns in tables and graphs to make predictions

- Use graphing calculators to investigate linear relationships

- Communicate with and interpret information from a variety of representations

- Recognize linear situations in all forms of representation: written descriptions, tables, graphs, and symbols

- Recognize that linearity is associated with a constant rate of change between two variables

- Recognize a change in the slope or the y-intercept and its effect on the various representations

- Solve a linear function of the form $y = mx + b$ using tables, graphs, and equations

- Find the slope of a line from a graph, a table, or an equation and interpret its meaning

- Find the y-intercept of a linear equation from its table, graph, or equation and interpret its meaning

- Write a linear equation given the slope and y-intercept

- Reason with different representations to interpret linear relationships

- Find a solution common to two linear equations by graphing or creating tables

The overall goal of the Connected Mathematics curriculum is to help students develop sound mathematical habits. Through their work in this and other algebra units, students learn important questions to ask themselves about any situation that can be represented and modeled mathematically, such as: *How can an equation express a relationship we see in the everyday world? When two related quantities change, how can we tell whether the change is predictable? How can we tell whether it can be expressed by a mathematical equation? How can the graph made from a table of specific values help us predict other values? How accurate can such predictions be? Can graphs help us predict changes between related variables if the variables are not related in a linear way? What does it mean to solve an equation? What tools can be used to solve equations? How can one decide which tool or method is best? What kinds of everyday problems can be solved by using mathematical tables and equations?*

The ideas in *Moving Straight Ahead* build on and connect to several big ideas in other Connected Mathematics units.

Big Idea	Prior Work	Future Work
identifying, representing, and interpreting linear relationships in tabular, graphical, and symbolic forms	graphing data in the coordinate plane; using symbols to represent relationships between variables (*Variables and Patterns; Accentuate the Negative*)	identifying and interpreting equations for linear ($y = mx + b$), exponential ($y = a^x$), quadratic ($y = ax^2 + bx + c$), and nonlinear (e.g., $y = \frac{k}{x}$) relationships (*Thinking with Mathematical Models; Growing, Growing, Growing; Frogs, Fleas, and Painted Cubes; Say It with Symbols*)
writing and interpreting linear equations in $y = mx + b$ form	expressing relationships between variables in words, symbols, graphs, and tables (*Variables and Patterns*)	writing and interpreting equations that express linear, non-linear, quadratic, and exponential relationships (*Thinking with Mathematical Models; Growing, Growing, Growing; Frogs, Fleas, and Painted Cubes; Say It with Symbols*)
finding and interpreting the point of intersection of two lines	understanding the meaning of parallel and intersecting lines (*Shapes and Designs*)	finding and interpreting points of intersection in graphs and mathematical models (*Thinking with Mathematical Models*); interpreting parallel, intersecting, and perpendicular lines (*Looking for Pythagoras*); analyzing equivalent linear expressions (*Say It with Symbols*)
finding the slope of a line; interpreting slope as the ratio of vertical change to horizontal change	computing and interpreting ratios (*Bits and Pieces I; Bits and Pieces II; Comparing and Scaling*); finding rates of change in relationships between variables (*Variables and Patterns*); understanding positive and negative numbers (*Accentuate the Negative*)	analyzing linear models; interpreting slope as a rate of change (*Thinking with Mathematical Models*); interpreting slope in linear relationships (*Looking for Pythagoras*); finding the slope of a line to determine an equation in $y = mx + b$ form (*Say It with Symbols*)
identifying x- and y-intercepts from a graph or an equation	graphing relationships between variables (*Variables and Patterns*)	interpreting and constructing graphs of lines; determining the equation of a line (*Thinking with Mathematical Models; Say It with Symbols*)

Investigation 1: Predicting from Patterns

This investigation poses the unit's central question of how we can determine whether a relationship is linear. The class conducts one or two experiments and observes that the data collected appear to lie in a straight line. At this stage, a linear relationship is described as one whose graph is a straight line. Students use tables and graphs to make sense of and to make predictions from the data they collect.

Investigation 2: Walking Rates

Students take a closer look at rates in multiple representations, revisiting situations similar to some of those they encountered in the *Variables and Patterns* unit. The rates at which people walk and the pledge per mile paid by sponsors of a walkathon are two of the contexts for this investigation. Students explore constant rate of change in tables, graphs, and equations. They investigate the change in the rate and its effect on various representations. The y-intercept is introduced informally in problems that ask students to interpret the information represented by points on a line, entries in a table, or solutions to an equation, and how these representations are related.

Investigation 3: Exploring Lines with a Graphing Calculator

Students use the graphing calculator to explore the effects of changing m and b in graphs of the form $y = mx + b$. They also use the calculator to find points on a graph and relate the information in the coordinates to the situation and to other representations. The intersection of two lines is introduced, and students use the graphing calculator to find the intersection point. The final problem brings together all of the ideas in the investigation.

Investigation 4: Solving Equations

Students develop a symbolic method for solving an equation of the form $y = mx + b$ using the idea of "undoing the operations." They are first asked to solve this problem in any way they choose: "How many months will it take to pay for an item costing $195 if you pay $30 down and $15 a month?" Their arithmetic reasoning is then applied to the equation $195 = 30 + 15n$, which leads naturally to a "balancing the equation" method of solving an equation. This method is developed more fully in the grade 8 *Say It with Symbols* unit.

Investigation 5: Exploring Slope

Students continue to develop their understanding of what it means for a situation to be linear: there must be a constant rate of change between the two variables: for each unit change in x, there must be a constant rate of change in y. The steepness of a set of stairs is used to model the concept of the slope of a line. Students find the constant rate or slope from a table; find the slope of a line given two points; and determine whether a line is increasing (has a positive slope), decreasing (has a negative slope), or neither (has a slope of 0).

Investigation 6: Writing an Equation for a Line

In this investigation, students find the equation of a line from two pieces of information: the slope and the y-intercept. First, students work with a given y-intercept and determine the slope of the line. Gradually, they develop methods for finding the y-intercept from a table or graph. Once they have the slope and y-intercept, they can write the equation of the line. For example, the y-intercept can be found by the rates in a table to get to the entry $(0, b)$. The slope is found either by generating a table or using the ratio of vertical change to horizontal change.

Materials

For students

- Blank sheets of transparency film and transparency markers (optional)
- Large sheets of paper (optional)
- Materials for the experiments in Investigation 1: 12-oz waxed paper cups, paper clips, clear graduated cylinders or other measuring containers, clocks or other timers, water, balls (golf balls, table tennis balls, tennis balls), and metersticks
- Rulers or tape measures
- String
- Graphing calculators (with the capacity to display a function as a table)
- Grid paper (provided as blackline masters)

For the teacher

- Transparencies and transparency markers (optional)
- Transparent grids (optional; copy the grids onto transparency film)
- Overhead display model of the students' graphing calculator (optional)
- Strips of balsa wood (optional)

Technology

Connected Mathematics was developed with the belief that calculators should always be available and that students should decide when to use them.

This unit requires a graphing calculator. This tool gives students a useful method for finding information about a situation by drawing and examining the related graph. It also allows students to explore many examples quickly and to observe patterns and make conjectures about functions (in this unit, linear functions). In the teaching notes, examples using the Texas Instruments TI-80 and TI-82 graphing calculators show teachers how to help students use the calculators. If other types of graphing calculators are used, see the reference manuals for instruction. If your calculators cannot generate tables, have students create tables for some of the problems by hand. It is important for them to make connections between the tables and the graphs.

If you have computers available, there are several interesting software programs that can help students develop their understanding. See the resources below.

Resources

Books

Winter, Mary Jean, and Ronald J. Carlson. *Algebra Experiments I: Exploring Linear Functions.* Menlo Park, Calif.: Addison-Wesley, 1993.

Heid, Kathleen. *Algebra in a Technological World: NCTM Addenda Series Grades 9–12.* Reston, Va.: National Council of Teachers of Mathematics, 1995.

Software packages

Dugale, Sharon, and David Kibbey. *Green Globs and Graphing Equations* (IBM, Apple II, Macintosh). Pleasantville, N.Y.: Sunburst Communications.

Rosenberg, Jon. *Math Connections: Algebra I* (Macintosh). Pleasantville, N.Y.: Sunburst Communications.

Pacing Chart

This pacing chart gives estimates of the class time required for each investigation and assessment piece. Shaded rows indicate opportunities for assessment.

Investigations and Assessments	Class Time
1 Predicting from Patterns	2 days
2 Walking Rates	6 days
Check-Up	$\frac{1}{2}$ day
3 Exploring Lines with a Graphing Calculator	5 days
Quiz A	1 day
4 Solving Equations	5 days
5 Exploring Slope	3 days
Quiz B	1 day
6 Writing an Equation for a Line	4 days
Self-Assessment	Take home
Unit Test	1 day

Moving Straight Ahead Vocabulary

The following words and concepts are used in *Moving Straight Ahead*. Concepts in the left column are those essential for student understanding of this and future units. The Descriptive Glossary gives descriptions of many of these words.

Essential terms developed in this unit	Terms developed in previous units	Nonessential terms
coefficient	axes	constant term
coordinate pair	equation	function
linear, linear relationship	graph, coordinate graph	origin
point of intersection	independent variable, dependent variable	scale
rise	intersection	steepness
run	inverse operations	symbolic method
slope	pattern	*x*-intercept
y-intercept	ratio, rate	
	table	
	variable	

Assessment Summary

Embedded Assessment

Opportunities for informal assessment of student progress are embedded throughout *Moving Straight Ahead* in the problems, ACE questions, and Mathematical Reflections. Suggestions for observing as students explore and discover mathematical ideas, for probing to guide their progress in developing concepts and skills, and for questioning to determine their level of understanding can be found in the Launch, Explore, or Summarize sections of all investigation problems. Some examples:

- Investigation 3, Problem 3.4 *Launch* (page 52g) suggests questions you can ask to assess and help clarify your students' understanding of the meaning of the *y*-intercept and the coefficient of *x* in the general equation $y = mx + b$.

- Investigation 4, Problem 4.2 *Explore* (page 63c) suggests ways you might help students verbalize their developing understanding of how to solve linear equations.

- Investigation 2, Problem 2.2 *Summarize* (page 34c) suggests questions you can ask to assess and further develop your students' understanding of the effect of a constant rate of change in three representations: tables, graphs, and equations.

ACE Assignments

An ACE (Applications–Connections–Extensions) section appears at the end of each investigation. To help you assign ACE questions, a list of assignment choices is given in the margin next to the reduced student page for each problem. Each list indicates the ACE questions that students should be able to answer after they complete the problem.

Check-Up

One check-up, which may be given after Investigation 2, is provided for use as a quick quiz or warm-up activity. The check-up is designed for students to complete individually. You will find the check-up and its answer key in the Assessment Resources section.

Partner Quizzes

Two quizzes, which may be given after Investigations 3 and 5, are provided with *Moving Straight Ahead*. These quizzes are designed to be completed by pairs of students with the opportunity for revision based on teacher feedback. You will find the quizzes and their answers in the Assessment Resources section. As an alternative to the quizzes provided, you can construct your own quizzes by combining questions from the Question Bank, these quizzes, and unassigned ACE questions.

Question Bank

A Question Bank provides questions you can use for homework, reviews, or quizzes. You will find the Question Bank and its answer key in the Assessment Resources section.

Notebook/Journal

Students should have notebooks to record and organize their work. Notebooks should include student journals and sections for vocabulary, homework, and check-ups. In their journals, students can take notes, solve investigation problems, and record their ideas about Mathematical Reflections questions. Journals should be assessed for completeness rather than correctness; they should be seen as "safe" places where students can try out their thinking. A Notebook Checklist and a Self-Assessment are provided in the Assessment Resources section. The Notebook Checklist helps students organize their notebooks. The Self-Assessment guides students as they review their notebooks to determine which ideas they have mastered and which ideas they still need to work on.

The Unit Test

The final assessment for *Moving Straight Ahead* is a unit test, which focuses on using and solving linear equations by examining tables and graphs and manipulating symbols to simplify equations.

Introducing Your Students to *Moving Straight Ahead*

This introduction will raise issues relating to linear relationships that will be clarified by the end of the unit. To begin the unit, you will want to remind students of some of the relationships they investigated in the *Variables and Patterns* unit, such as the relationship between speed and distance or between the numbers of bikes rented and the rental cost. This will allow them to build on the ideas and vocabulary they already have.

Spend a few minutes with the class discussing the three examples. Be alert to methods they suggest for solving the problems. What kind of reasoning do they use? Do they suggest using tables or graphs? Do they suggest effective use of symbols?

Moving Straight Ahead

Henri challenges his older brother Emile to a walking race. Emile figures out that his walking rate is 2.5 meters per second, and Henri's walking rate is 1 meter per second. Emile agrees to give Henri a 45-meter head start. Emile knows Henri would enjoy winning the race, but he does not want to make the race so short that it is obvious his brother will win. What distance would allow Henri to win in a close race?

Rosa's grandfather gives her some money as a birthday gift. She plans to put her birthday money in a safe place and add the same amount from her allowance to it each week. After five weeks, she will have a total of $175, and after eight weeks, she will have $190. How much money is Rosa planning to save each week? How much money did her grandfather give her for her birthday?

To estimate the outside temperature, count cricket chirps. If a cricket chirps n times in one minute, then the temperature, t, in degrees Fahrenheit can be computed with the formula $t = \frac{1}{4}n + 40$. What is the temperature if a cricket chirps 150 times in a minute?

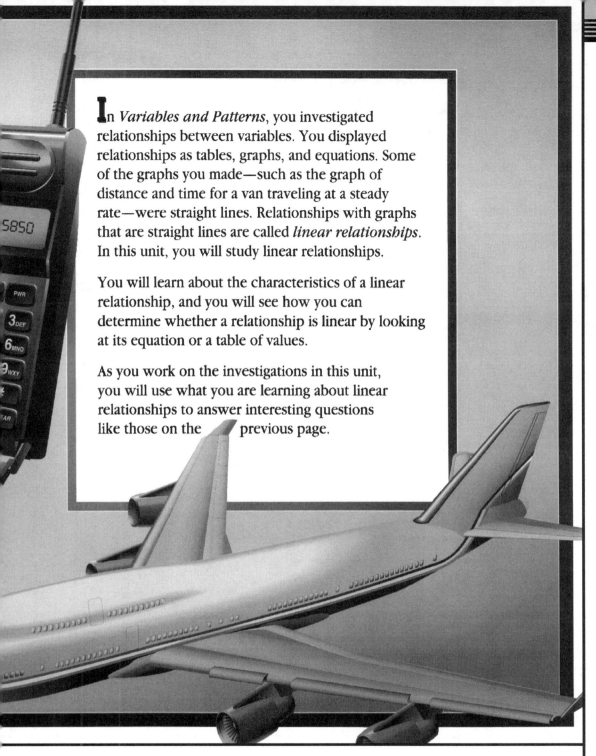

In *Variables and Patterns*, you investigated relationships between variables. You displayed relationships as tables, graphs, and equations. Some of the graphs you made—such as the graph of distance and time for a van traveling at a steady rate—were straight lines. Relationships with graphs that are straight lines are called *linear relationships*. In this unit, you will study linear relationships.

You will learn about the characteristics of a linear relationship, and you will see how you can determine whether a relationship is linear by looking at its equation or a table of values.

As you work on the investigations in this unit, you will use what you are learning about linear relationships to answer interesting questions like those on the previous page.

Explain to the class that these are all examples of linear relationships and that the purpose of this unit is for students to be able to determine—by inspecting tables, graphs, and equations—which situations are linear and which are not linear. They will learn to represent linear situations by tables, graphs, and equations and to reason about these situations using any of these representations. They will also discover that linear relationships occur in many situations that they may not have expected.

Mathematical Highlights

The Mathematical Highlights page provides information for students and for parents and other family members. It gives students a preview of the activities and problems in *Moving Straight Ahead*. As they work through the unit, students can refer back to the Mathematical Highlights page to review what they have learned and to preview what is still to come. This page also tells students' families what mathematical ideas and activities will be covered as the class works through *Moving Straight Ahead*.

Mathematical Highlights

In *Moving Straight Ahead* you will explore properties of the most important type of relationship among variables, linearity. The unit should help you to

- Recognize problem situations in which two or more variables have a linear relationship to each other;

- Construct tables, graphs, and symbolic equations that express linear relationships;

- Translate information about linear relations given in a table, a graph, or an equation to one of the other forms;

- Understand the connections between linear equations and patterns in the tables and graphs of those relations—rate of change, slope, and y-intercept;

- Solve linear equations;

- Solve problems and make decisions about linear relationships using information given in tables, graphs, and symbolic expressions; and

- Use a graphing calculator to make tables and graphs of linear relations between variables and to answer questions about those relations.

As you work on the problems of this unit, ask questions about problem situations that involve related quantities: *What are the variables in the problem? Do the variables in this problem have a linear relationship to each other? What patterns in the problem suggest that it is linear? How can the linear pattern in a table, graph, or problem statement be expressed with an equation? How can tables, graphs, and equations of linear relationships be used to express and answer given questions?*

The Investigations

The teaching materials for each investigation consist of three parts: an overview, student pages with teaching outlines, and detailed notes for teaching the investigation.

The overview of each investigation includes brief descriptions of the problems, the mathematical and problem-solving goals of the investigation, and a list of necessary materials.

Essential information for teaching the investigation is provided in the margins around the student pages. The "At a Glance" overviews are brief outlines of the Launch, Explore, and Summarize phases of each problem for reference as you work with the class. To help you assign homework, a list of "Assignment Choices" is provided next to each problem. Wherever space permits, answers to problems, follow-ups, ACE questions, and Mathematical Reflections appear next to the appropriate student pages.

The Teaching the Investigation section follows the student pages and is the heart of the Connected Mathematics curriculum. This section describes in detail the Launch, Explore, and Summarize phases for each problem. It includes all the information needed for teaching, along with suggestions for what you might say at key points in the teaching. Use this section to prepare lessons and as a guide for teaching investigations.

Assessment Resources

The Assessment Resources section contains blackline masters and answer keys for the check-up, quizzes, the Question Bank, and the Unit Test. Blackline masters for the Notebook Checklist and the Self-Assessment are given. These instruments support student self-evaluation, an important aspect of assessment in the Connected Mathematics curriculum. A discussion of how one teacher assessed students' work on the check-up and a quiz is included, along with sample pages of the students' work.

Blackline Masters

The Blackline Masters section includes masters for all labsheets and transparencies. Blackline masters of centimeter and half-centimeter grid paper are also provided.

Additional Practice

Practice pages for each investigation offer additional problems for students who need more practice with the basic concepts developed in the investigations as well as some continual review of earlier concepts.

Descriptive Glossary

The Descriptive Glossary provides descriptions and examples of the key concepts in *Moving Straight Ahead*. These descriptions are not intended to be formal definitions, but are meant to give you an idea of how students might make sense of these important concepts.

Predicting from Patterns

The two experiments in Problem 1.1, Conducting an Experiment, were chosen because the graphs made from the collected data are convincingly linear in appearance. In Problem 1.1A, Wasting Water, students conduct an experiment to simulate the relationship between time and the amount of water lost from a leaking faucet. The experiment produces a graph that appears linear and permits predictions to be made beyond the data collected. In Problem 1.1B, Bouncing Balls, students investigate the relationship between the drop height of a ball and its bounce height, which is controlled by the fraction of the ball's energy that is lost on impact. This fraction varies for different balls but is constant for an individual ball. The graphs for this experiment should theoretically be linear and pass through the origin; even with measurement errors, the graphs should allow students to make predictions confidently.

The questions posed in the problems and the ACE section focus on making predictions from observed patterns.

Mathematical and Problem-Solving Goals

- **To encounter the idea that many phenomena are constrained by linear relationships**

- **To collect data and use patterns in tables and graphs to make predictions**

- **To connect points on a graph of data that were collected or predicted**

Materials		
Problem	**For students**	**For the teacher**
All	Graphing calculators, grid paper (provided as black-line masters), blank transparencies (optional)	Transparencies 1.1A to 1.1D (optional)
1.1A	12-oz waxed paper cups, paper clips, clear graduated cylinders or other small measuring containers, clocks or other timers, water	
1.1B	Balls (such as golf balls, table tennis balls, tennis balls), metersticks	

INVESTIGATION 1

Predicting from Patterns

All around you, things occur in patterns. Once you observe a pattern, you can predict information beyond and between the data observed. The ability to use patterns to make predictions makes it possible for you to run to the right position to catch a fly ball or to guess how a story will end. Often, you are not even aware that you are thinking about patterns until something surprises you because it does not fit a familiar pattern. For example, the first time you bounced a superball, you may have had trouble catching it because you weren't expecting it to bounce so high. You were basing your expectations on patterns you had observed for other types of balls.

In many situations, patterns become apparent only after sufficient data are collected, organized, and displayed. In this investigation, you will conduct an experiment and use patterns in the data to make predictions.

1.1 Conducting an Experiment

Problems 1.1A and 1.1B are experiments. Your group should carry out *only one* of these experiments. Read the directions carefully *before you start.* Be prepared to explain your findings to the rest of the class.

- In Problem 1.1A, you investigate the rate at which a leaking faucet loses water.
- In Problem 1.1B, you investigate how the drop height of a ball is related to its bounce height.

At a Glance

Grouping: groups of 3

Launch

- Read the introduction, and discuss observing and predicting from patterns.
- Have students do ACE question 1. *(optional)*
- Allow students to choose an experiment (or decide which single experiment the class will conduct).

Explore

- Ask groups to put their data and predictions on transparencies. *(optional)*
- Have groups do ACE question 4. *(optional)*

Summarize

- Let groups share their results.
- Use the data to make predictions.
- Discuss the methods students used to make predictions and patterns they see in the data.

Assignment Choices

ACE questions 1–9

1.1A: Wasting Water

In this experiment, you will simulate a leaking faucet and collect data about the volume of water lost at 5-second intervals. You will then use the patterns in your results to predict how much water is wasted when a faucet leaks for one month.

Equipment: a paper cup, water, a sharp object (such as a paper clip or a small nail), a clear measuring container, and a watch or clock with a second hand

Directions: You will need to figure out how to divide the work among the members of your group.

1. Make a table with columns for recording time and amount of water lost. Fill in the time column with values from 0 seconds to 60 seconds in 5-second intervals (that is, 5, 10, 15, and so on).
2. Use the sharp object to punch a small hole in the bottom of the cup. Cover the hole with your finger.
3. Fill the paper cup with water.
4. Hold the paper cup over the measuring container.
5. When you are ready to begin timing, uncover the hole so that the water drips into the measuring container.
6. In a table, record the amount of water in the measuring container at 5-second intervals, up to a total time of 60 seconds.

> ### Problem 1.1A
>
> **A.** Make a coordinate graph of the data you collected.
>
> **B.** What variables did you investigate in this experiment? Describe the relationship between the variables.
>
> **C.** If a faucet dripped at the same rate as your cup does, how much water would be wasted in 2 minutes? In 2.5 minutes? In 3 minutes and 15 seconds? Explain how you made your predictions. Did you use the table, the graph, or some other method? What clues in the data helped you?

Answers to Problem 1.1A

A. See page 14d.

B. The variables are amount of water lost and time. As time increases, more water is lost.

C. Answers will vary. Students should be using the pattern for the rate at which water is lost in the first 60 seconds to predict the amount lost for greater increments of time. This is straightforward to do from the table since time is noted at evenly spaced intervals. The graph would be helpful whether the time intervals for the data collection were chosen in an organized way or not.

Problem 1.1A Follow-Up

1. If a faucet dripped into the measuring container at the same rate as your paper cup does, how long would it take for the container to overflow?
2. Besides time, what other variables affect the amount of water in the measuring container?
3. If a faucet leaked at the same rate as your paper cup, how much water would be wasted in one month? Explain how you arrived at your answer.
4. Find out how much water costs in your area. Use this information and your answer from question 3 to figure out the cost of the water wasted by a leaking faucet in one month.

1.1B: Bouncing Balls

You have probably bounced lots of kinds of balls. After bouncing a ball many times, you are better able to predict its behavior. For example, practicing bouncing a basketball can help you make a more accurate bounce pass in a game. In this experiment, you will investigate how the height from which a ball is dropped is related to the height it bounces.

Equipment: a meterstick and a ball that bounces

Directions: You will need to figure out how to divide up the work among the members of your group.

1. Make a table with columns for recording drop height and bounce height.
2. Hold the meterstick perpendicular to a flat surface, such as an uncarpeted floor, a table, or a desk.
3. Choose and record a height on the meterstick as the height from which you will drop the ball. Hold the ball at this height.
4. *Drop* the ball, and record the height of the first bounce. (You may have to do this several times before you feel confident you can make a good estimate of the bounce height.)
5. Repeat this for several different drop heights.

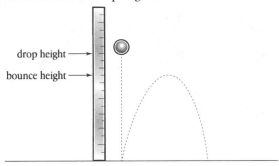

drop height ⟶

bounce height ⟶

Investigation 1: Predicting from Patterns 7

Answers to Problem 1.1A Follow-Up

1. Answers will vary. If a 100-ml container were used in the example given in the answer to part A of the problem, it would take about 2 min 15 s for the container to overflow.

2. Possible answer: The size of the hole and how much water is in the cup initially could affect the amount of water in the container.

3. Answers will vary. Students' solution should use their data. For example, they might take the amount of water lost in 1 minute and multiply it by 60 to get the amount lost in an hour, by 24 to get a day's loss, and then by 30 to find the amount lost in a month. The graph alone will not be useful, as 1 month is not easily located on a scale using 5-second intervals.

4. Answers will vary.

Problem 1.1B

A. Make a coordinate graph of the data you collected.

B. What variables did you investigate in this experiment? Describe the relationship between the variables.

C. Predict the bounce height for a drop height of 2 meters. Explain how you made your prediction. Did you use the table, the graph, or some other method? What clues in the data helped you?

D. Predict the drop height needed for a bounce height of 2 meters. Explain how you made your prediction. Did you use the table, the graph, or some other method? What clues in the data helped you?

E. What bounce height would you expect for a drop height of 0 centimeters? Where would this be on the graph?

■ **Problem 1.1B Follow-Up**
Besides the drop height, what other variables affect the bounce height of the ball?

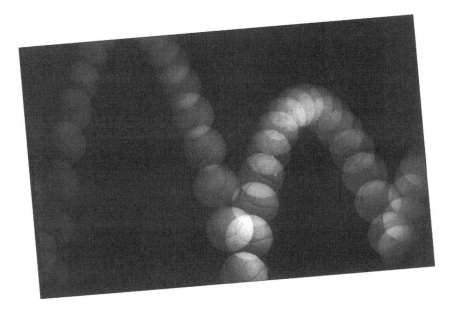

Answers to Problem 1.1B

See page 14d.

Answer to Problem 1.1B Follow-Up

Possible answer: The material from which the ball is constructed, the surface on which the ball bounces, and the way the data are collected (students may collect several pieces of data for each bounce and average them; some may use the top of the ball to measure the drop and bounce heights) could all affect the bounce height.

As you work on these ACE questions, use your calculator whenever you need it.

Applications

1. The table of data below was produced by students who did the bouncing-ball experiment.

Drop height (centimeters)	20	30	40	50	60	70	80
Bounce height (centimeters)	10	18	25	32	38	45	50

   a. Make a coordinate graph of these data.

   b. Predict the bounce height for a drop height of 45 centimeters. What method did you use to make your prediction?

   c. Predict the bounce height for a drop height of 140 centimeters.

   d. Predict the drop height needed for a bounce height of 60 centimeters.

   e. Are you equally confident about each prediction you made in parts b–d? Explain.

2. The table of data below was produced by students who did the leaking-faucet experiment. The measuring container they used held only 100 milliliters. If the students had continued their experiment, after how many seconds would the measuring container have overflowed?

Time (seconds)	10	20	30	40	50	60	70
Water loss (milliliters)	2	5	8.5	11.5	14	16.5	19.5

3. **a.** Think of two variables whose relationship can be represented by a straight-line graph like the one at the right. Copy the graph, and add labels for the variables you chose.

   b. Make up a question about your variables that could be answered by using the graph.

1a.

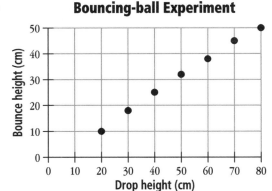

Bouncing-ball Experiment

3a. Possible answer:

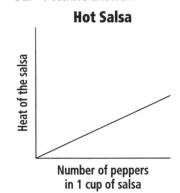

Hot Salsa

Answers

Applications

1a. See below left.

1b. Possible answer: 28.5 cm; I took the value halfway between 25 cm and 32 cm in the table.

1c. Possible answer: 92 cm; I continued the drop heights in the table up to 140 cm and then decided the rate at which to increase the bounce heights. The bounce appears to increase about 7 cm for every increase of 10 cm in the drop height.

1d. Possible answer: 95 cm

1e. Possible answer: The answer to part b involved data between known points (and thus involved interpolation), so I feel confident about it. I'm less confident about parts c and d. The answer for part c was far from the known data (extrapolation). For part d, the table is not set up conveniently for finding a drop height for a known bounce height, so the graph was easier to use.

2. Possible answer: At 70 s approximately 20 ml have been lost. At that rate it will take about 70 × 5 = 350 s, or 5 min 50 s, for the container to overflow. (Note: Students may draw a graph and extend it, or they may reason from the table.)

3a. See left.

3b. Possible question: "Will the salsa taste hotter or milder when more peppers are added?"

Connections

4a. See below right.

4b. See below right.

4c. distance = 60 × time, or $d = 60t$

4d. 60 × 8 = 480 mi

4e. $\frac{300}{60}$ = 5 h

4f. Answers will vary. Any pair of values in the table represents a point on the graph and will satisfy the rule.

5a. See page 14e.

5b. Possible answer: This table and graph show profit increasing as the number of T-shirts sold increases. In the experiments, the rate of increase was not exactly constant, so the graph was not exactly a straight line. (Note: Students may also mention, in their own words, the scale on the axes and the slope of line.)

5c. Possible answer: The tables both show steady increases, one in distance and the other in profit. The rate of increase is different in the two situations. Both graphs are straight lines. The rules are similar, but one multiplies time by 60 while the other multiplies number of T-shirts sold by 5.

Connections

4. In *Variables and Patterns*, you saw that the distance traveled by the tour van depended on time. Suppose the van averaged a steady 60 miles per hour on the interstate highway. The table below shows the relationship between the time traveled and the distance.

Time (hours)	0.5	1.0	1.5	2.0	2.5	3.0	3.5
Distance (miles)	30	60					

a. Copy and complete the table.

b. Make a coordinate graph of the data in the table.

c. Write a rule that describes the relationship between distance and time.

d. Predict the distance traveled in 8 hours.

e. Predict the time needed to travel 300 miles.

f. Pick a pair of (time, distance) values from the table. How is the pair related to the graph and the rule?

5. The soccer boosters make $5 on each T-shirt they sell. This can be described by the equation $A = 5n$, where A is the amount of money made and n is the number of T-shirts sold.

a. Make a table and a graph showing the amount of money made by selling up to ten T-shirts.

b. Compare the table and the graph from part a with the table and the graph you made for your experiment in Problem 1.1A or 1.1B. How are the tables similar? How are they different? How are the graphs similar? How are they different? What do you think causes the similarities and differences?

c. Compare the table, graph, and rule for the T-shirt sale with the table, graph, and rule in question 4. Describe the similarities and differences.

4a.

Time (hours)	0.5	1.0	1.5	2.0	2.5	3.0	3.5
Distance (miles)	30	60	90	120	150	180	210

4b.

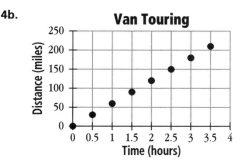

6. Denise and Takashi worked together on the leaking-faucet experiment. Each of them made a graph of the data they collected. What might have caused their graphs to look so different?

Denise's Graph

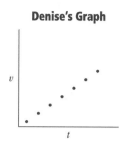

Takashi's Graph

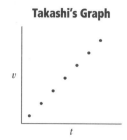

7. What might the following graph mean with regard to the leaking-faucet experiment?

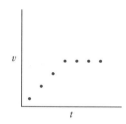

8. Jack does the bouncing-ball experiment and collects the following data.

Drop height (centimeters)	30	40	50	60	70	80	90
Bounce height (centimeters)	20	24	31	37	43	51	60

Jack says he does not need to make a graph to predict the bounce height for a drop height of 130 centimeters. He says the rule is that the bounce height is always two thirds of the drop height. Is his rule reasonable? Explain.

6. Possible answer: The difference might just be the scale the students used on their axes.

7. Possible answers: This could mean that no more water was lost after a certain time, perhaps because the cup was finally empty or the hole had been plugged. Or, if *v* refers to *volume collected* in the measuring container, the container might have overflowed, so no more water could be collected.

8. Possible answer: Jack's rule works for two data pairs but gives greater bounce heights than were actually observed in the other five data pairs. His rule is reasonable, but a value slightly less than two thirds may create smaller discrepancies between what the rule predicts will happen and what actually happened.

9a. The variables are weight and length of the spring. In general, as weight is added, the length of the spring increases.

Extensions

9. Mr. Delgrosso's class conducted an experiment using a spring and some weights. They placed each weight on the end of the spring and measured the length of the stretched spring.

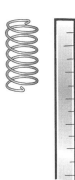 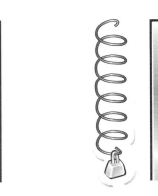

a. One student made the graph below to display the class's data from the experiment. What are the variables? Describe the general relationship between the variables.

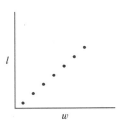

b. Another student used the same data to make the graph below. How is this graph different from the graph in part a? Is it possible that both graphs are correct? Explain.

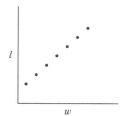

Possible Answers

1. The tables of linear relationships show a constant increase (or decrease) in how one variable relates to the other. In the experiments, the differences were not quite constant, but in the tables in the ACE questions, the differences in the tables were constant.

2. Distance to school is related to the time it takes to get to school, and the number of minutes you read a book is related to the number of pages you read. (Note: Students may offer suggestions that are not really linear but in which they feel certain that one variable depends on the other. All the examples in this investigation have been direct relationships—one variable increasing with the other—so students will probably stay with that idea.)

Mathematical Reflections

In this investigation, you conducted an experiment. By organizing your data into a table and a graph, you observed patterns and used the patterns to make predictions. These questions will help you summarize what you have learned:

1 One of the goals of this unit is to discover ways to identify a linear relationship from its table. Look at the table you made for your experiment and the tables you have made for other straight-line relationships. What do you think characterizes the table of a linear relationship?

2 What other relationships that you have investigated, in this class or somewhere else, do you now suspect to be linear?

Think about your answers to these questions, discuss your ideas with other students and your teacher, and then write a summary of your findings in your journal.

Tips for the Linguistically Diverse Classroom

Diagram Code The Diagram Code technique is described in detail in *Getting to Know Connected Mathematics*. Students use a minimal number of words and drawings, diagrams, or symbols to respond to questions that require writing. Example: Question 2—A student might answer this question by drawing a school down a road from a house with two stick figures coming from the house. The student could write *1 mile* above the road, *walks 1 mile in 15 min* above one stick figure, and *walks 1 mile in 20 min* above the other stick figure.

TEACHING THE INVESTIGATION

1.1 • Conducting an Experiment

In the *Variables and Patterns* unit, students explored relationships among variables and found patterns to help them write the relationships in symbolic form. They used graphs, tables, and equations to represent situations. In the experiments in this problem, they will collect data, search for patterns in the resulting graphs and tables, and extend the patterns to make predictions from the collected data. To make such predictions possible, the rate of change between the dependent variable and the independent variable must be assumed to be constant.

You may want to have students do ACE question 1 before conducting their experiment. This has the advantage of offering students a review of tables, graphs, and the process of looking for patterns so that they more fully understand the goals of the experiments, but the disadvantage of being more directive.

Launch

To prepare for the follow-up to this problem, you may want to check on the cost of water in your community. (For example, water service might include a base charge plus a price per 100 cubic feet of water used, say $1.05.)

Read the introduction about observing and predicting from patterns. This will probably elicit other examples from students—examples in which they have learned to observe and extend patterns or in which they have been surprised by a pattern that did not continue as expected.

To simplify this activity, you may want to choose, or have the class choose, a single experiment to conduct. With the class, read the short description of the experiment(s).

> How accurately do you think you can predict the amount of water lost by a leaking faucet in a month?
>
> How accurately do you think you can predict the drop height of a ball necessary to create a particular bounce height?

This is the challenge of the experiments: to find patterns that are clear enough to allow reliable predictions to be made.

Talk to the class about experimental data. Since there will be errors in the data collected, the emphasis of the activity should be on collecting the data as carefully as possible and then looking for what seems like reasonable assumptions about the underlying relationships. The data and the patterns in the data should allow students to predict with a reasonable degree of confidence what would happen for particular values of the independent variable—*time* in the water experiment and *drop height* in the ball experiment—that are not in their data set.

Review the steps for setting up the experiment(s). You may want to help groups establish a consistent way of measuring, or you may want students to find out for themselves that they need to establish consistent procedures. Groups of three work well for these experiments.

For the leaking-faucet experiment, you might suggest that one team member reads the time at 5-second intervals, a second team member reads the volume of water in the container, and a

third records the data. You may want to test (or have students test) different ways of creating the hole in the bottom of the cup. Some teachers find it best to use a large paper clip to punch the hole; others use a small nail. Experiment with the cup by timing how long it takes for all the water to drain out; the experiment works well if it takes about a minute to fully empty. Narrow graduated cylinders make easily read containers for catching the water; alternatively, students could mark in milliliters whatever containers you have available. If the pressure of the water in the cup were constant, the relationship of time to water loss would be linear. However, the pressure decreases as the cup empties. You may want to have students add water to the cup during the experiment to keep the water level somewhat constant.

For the bouncing-ball experiment, you might suggest that students always measure drop height and bounce height from the bottom of the ball as shown in the illustration on page 7. Emphasize that the ball should be dropped, not thrown, so that the only force acting on the ball is gravity. In this experiment, one team member could drop the ball, the second could measure the height of the bounce, and the third could record the data.

Sometimes the first trial of an experiment is flawed, but students will see from this trial what they need to do to collect data more accurately.

Have students work in groups of three on their chosen experiment.

Explore

Give groups time to talk about the mechanics of the experiment and to reach agreement about how to use the data to make predictions. Issues such as those mentioned in the launch may arise at this time. As much as possible, let students make their own decisions. If their decisions are wise (such as organizing the table, choosing an appropriate unit, or always measuring the same way), they will find predictions easier to make. Otherwise, they may experience frustration, but they will have a better understanding of how to conduct an experiment.

You may want to ask groups to put their data and predictions on blank transparencies to facilitate sharing of the results and to give you a check on how they organized their data. As groups finish, you may want to have them work on ACE question 4.

Summarize

When all groups have finished their experiment and made their predictions, have them share and compare their results, displaying their work on transparencies if you have supplied them. Discuss any problems you notice, such as incorrect scales on axes or incorrect choices for independent and dependent variable.

Why are there differences among your predictions?

Several factors could contribute to variations in predictions. For example, the size of the hole will vary, as will the method of measuring. Different types of balls may have been used.

Discuss the *method* of making the predictions. Students will often use the graph because it blurs the effect of measurement errors and does not distract from the overall picture the way a table full of numbers can. Some groups may not have been systematic in how they gathered and recorded data for the bounce height, which will make the data in the table appear disorganized.

Students may have connected the points on their graphs but, for predictions far from the graphed points, they will likely use a best-fit approximation to point ahead at the desired answers. They may not physically extend the line but simply visualize where it would be. Capitalize on this by asking how they decided on the steepness (slope) of the line. Suggest other slightly different lines. The discussion should bring up some of the language about rate of change that you want to focus on; for example, in response to a line suggested by you, students may say that the line makes the volume of water lost "grow faster" than the data actually indicate.

Tables are not as easy to use as graphs to see patterns of change. Again, the *rate of change* is the focus in these experiments, and sufficient data must be collected in order for a clear pattern to emerge. This is not the time for establishing formal definitions about rate of change; instead, simply bring the idea of rate of change into prominence as a useful way to think about patterns. You might ask questions such as the following:

> About how much did the water level increase for every 5-second increase in time?

> About how much did the bounce height increase for every 10-centimeter (20-centimeter, 50-centimeter) increase in the drop height?

To see how your class is understanding the idea of experimenting to find data to help make predictions, you may want to use ACE question 4 as part of the summary.

> Compare the graphs of the leaking-faucet experiment, the bouncing-ball experiment, and the graph from ACE question 4. What similarities and differences do you see? *(The graphs should all be linear—approximately linear in the case of the experimental data—and should all be increasing.)*

> Compare the tables of the leaking-faucet experiment, the bouncing-ball experiment, and the table from ACE question 4. What similarities and differences do you see? *(The tables should all show one variable increasing as the other increases. The increments in the variables are constant in the ACE question, while they are not quite so regular in the experiments.)*

> For the tour van, is predicting from the experimental data more or less difficult than predicting from the table of data? Explain. *(Predicting from the table of data is probably easier because of the precise, constant rate of increase in both variables.)*

For follow-up question 4 in Problem 1.1A, you may want to give your students the cost of water in the local area to save time. You might also bring in a water bill and challenge students to find the information themselves.

This investigation and its ACE questions should allow you to review students' earlier work with independent and dependent variables, graphing, and tables of data, especially as these ideas relate to linear relationships.

Additional Answers

Answers to Problem 1.1A

A. Possible answer:

Time (seconds)	Water (ml)
5	5
10	9
15	14
20	18
25	22
30	26
35	30
40	33
45	36
50	39
55	43
60	46

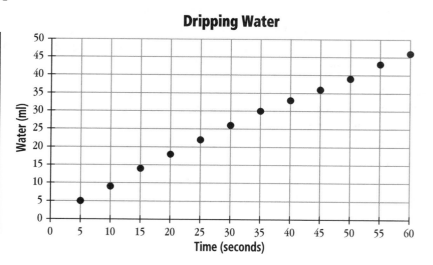

Answers to Problem 1.1B

A. The balls in the data below were dropped on a sidewalk. The bounce surface and
the surface of the ball will both affect the data.

| | Bounce height (cm) | |
Drop height (cm)	Table-tennis ball	Tennis ball
100	65	58
90	60	52
80	54	47
70	50	41
60	45	34

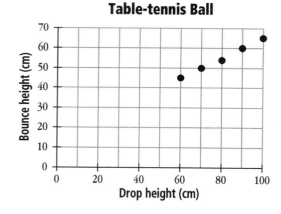

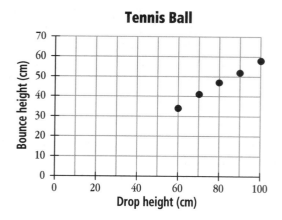

B. The variables are drop height and bounce height. As drop height increases, the ball bounces higher. Bounce height seems to increase at a constant rate.

C. Answers will vary. Students may use the table and the (approximately) constantly increasing bounce heights. However, if they did not organize the drop heights in constant intervals, the table will not be very helpful. The graph probably more clearly indicates a bounce height for a drop height of 2 m.

D. Answers will vary. Students will find the graph more convenient for answering this question because the drop height is the unknown and the data points are fairly linear.

E. If the drop height is 0 cm, the bounce height will also be 0 cm, which is at the point (0, 0) on the graph.

ACE Answers

Connections

5a.

T-shirts sold	1	2	3	4	5	6	7	8	9	10
Profit ($)	5	10	15	20	25	30	35	40	45	50

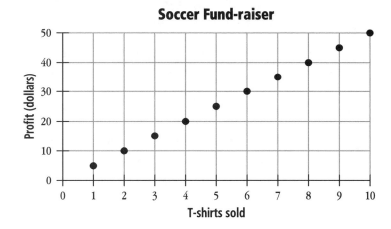

Soccer Fund-raiser

Walking Rates

In this investigation, students explore multiple representations—tables, graphs, and equations—in greater depth. They consider how changes in a situation affect the various representations, what each representation contributes to understanding the situation, and how each shows the relationship between variables in the situation. Students are also informally introduced to the concept of the *y*-intercept.

In Problem 2.1, Walking to the Yogurt Shop, students explore the effect of walking rates on time and distance walked. In Problem 2.2, Changing the Walking Rate, the distance walked for three walking rates is represented in a table, a graph, and equations, and students observe how the rate affects all three representations. In Problem 2.3, Walking for Charity, students look at suggestions for setting pledge amounts for a walkathon, which involves the rate of cost per mile. The cost-per-mile rate is compared to walking rates. The model $y = mx + b$ could represent both situations, where m is the rate at which a person walks or the cost per mile; both graphs are straight lines. In Problems 2.4 and 2.5, the context is a race in which one participant has a head start, which allows the introduction of the concept of the *y*-intercept. Problem 2.4, Walking to Win, presents the situation in an open-ended way, allowing students to think about what makes sense to them. In Problem 2.5, Crossing the Line, students explore what information a table, a graph, and an equation supply.

Mathematical and Problem-Solving Goals

- *To recognize linear relationships from tables: for each unit change in one variable, there is a constant rate of change in the other variable*

- *To determine whether a set of data is linear by examining its graph*

- *To recognize how the rate of change between two variables is associated with its representations*

- *To recognize that a change in rate will change the steepness of a line and the coefficient of x (the independent variable)*

- *To interpret the meaning of the coefficient of x and the y-intercept of a graph of y = mx + b*

Materials		
Problem	**For students**	**For the teacher**
All	Graphing calculators, grid paper (provided as black-line masters)	Transparencies 2.1 to 2.5 (optional), transparent grids (copy the grids onto transparency film), overhead graphing calculator (optional)
2.5	Blank transparencies or large sheets of paper (optional)	

▼ Student Pages 15–34   Teaching the Investigation 34a–34q

Walking Rates

In *Variables and Patterns,* you read about five college students who set up a bicycle-touring business. The students used tables, graphs, and equations to look for patterns relating variables such as cost, income, and profit.

For example, the total cost to rent bikes depends on the number of people on the tour. We say that the rental cost is a *function of* the number of people on the tour. The variables in this situation are the number of people and the cost. If you were interested in how these variables are related, you might ask questions like these:

As the number of people on the tour increases, what happens to the cost to rent the bikes?

If the tour partners want to decrease the cost of renting bikes, how will this affect the number of people who can go on the tour?

For example, one bike shop charges $300 plus $20 per bike to rent bikes for one week. If we let *C* be the total cost to rent the bikes and *n* the number of people who go on the tour, we can write this equation to show the relationship between the number of people on the tour and the total rental cost:

$$C = 300 + 20n$$

Remember that 20*n* means 20 *times n.* If a variable is multiplied by a number, we can omit the times sign.

In *Variables and Patterns*, you also looked at the number of miles a van covers in a specified period of time. For example, if a van averages 60 miles per hour, then the distance covered depends on the number of hours the van travels. In other words, the distance is a *function of* the number of hours of travel. The variables are distance traveled and time. The relationship between these variables can be expressed as

$$d = 60t$$

where d represents the distance traveled in miles and t represents the time in hours.

The graphs of $C = 300 + 20n$ and $d = 60t$ are straight lines.

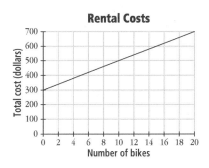

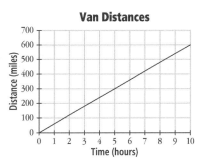

From the graphs, it is easy to see that the relationships between the number of bikes and the rental cost, and between the miles traveled and the time are **linear relationships**. In this investigation, you will consider this question:

How can you determine whether a situation is linear by examining a table of data or an equation?

Once you have determined—from the table, the graph, or the equation—that a relationship is linear, you can explore this question:

How does changing one of the quantities in a situation affect the table, the graph, or the equation?

For example, how does changing the cost per bike affect the table, the graph, and the equation of the relationship between the number of customers and the total rental cost? How does increasing the average speed at which the van travels affect the table, the graph, and the equation of the relationship between distance and time?

2.1 Walking to the Yogurt Shop

Mr. Goldberg's gym class does an experiment to determine their walking rates. Here are the results for three students.

Name	Walking rate
Terry	1 meter per second
Jade	2 meters per second
Jerome	2.5 meters per second

Jerome wonders how a person's walking rate would affect the amount of time it takes him or her to walk from school to the frozen yogurt shop.

Problem 2.1

A. If Terry, Jade, and Jerome leave school together and walk toward the frozen yogurt shop at the rates given in the table, how far apart will they be after 1 minute?

B. If the yogurt shop is 750 meters from school, how long will it take each student to walk there?

C. When Jerome arrives at the yogurt shop, how far away will Terry be?

Problem 2.1 Follow-Up

1. In Problem 2.1, what strategies did you use to get your answers?
2. Does Problem 2.1 involve linear relationships? Explain why or why not.

Launch

- Read the story of the students' walking rates and the walk to the frozen yogurt shop.

Explore

- Let students explore the problem using whatever methods make sense to them.
- Challenge groups that finish early to write other questions that can be answered by the data.

Summarize

- Have students discuss their strategies for solving the problem and share their ideas about whether the relationships in the problem are linear.

Answers to Problem 2.1

A. In 1 min, Terry will walk 60 m, Jade will walk 120 m, and Jerome will walk 150 m. After 1 min, Jerome and Jade will be 30 m apart. Jade will be 60 m ahead of Terry, and Terry will be 90 m behind Jerome.

B. It will take Terry 750 ÷ 1 = 750 s (or 12.5 min), Jade 750 ÷ 2 = 375 s (6.25 min), and Jerome 750 ÷ 2.5 = 300 s (5 min) to walk the 750 m.

C. In 5 min, Terry walks 300 m, so she will be 450 m from the frozen yogurt shop when Jerome arrives.

Answers to Problem 2.1 Follow-Up

See the Summarize section for possible responses.

Assignment Choices

ACE questions 14–17 and unassigned choices from earlier problems

Grouping: individuals, then small groups

Launch

■ Introduce the idea of the effect of walking rate on time and distance walked.

■ Talk with the class about which variable to put on which axis.

Explore

■ Have students work individually to make a table and a graph and to write equations.

■ In their groups, have students share their answers to the problem and then work on the follow-up.

Summarize

■ As a class, talk about how the constant rates of change show up in the table, graph, and equations.

■ Talk about the nonlinear example in the follow-up.

■ Offer other examples of nonlinear data. *(optional)*

2.2 Changing the Walking Rate

In Problem 2.1, you saw that a person's walking rate determines the time it takes him or her to walk a given distance. In this problem, you will more closely examine the effect that walking rate has on the relationship between time and distance walked. Your findings will give you some important clues about how to identify linear relationships from tables, graphs, and equations.

Problem 2.2

A. In Problem 2.1, each student walked at a different rate. Use the walking rates given in that problem to make a table showing the distance walked by each student after different numbers of seconds. How does the walking rate affect the data in the table?

Time (seconds)	Distance (meters)		
	Terry	Jade	Jerome
0	0	0	0
1	1	2	2.5
2			
3			
.			
.			
.			

B. Graph the time and distance data for the three students on the same coordinate axes. Use a different color for each student's data. How does the walking rate affect the graphs?

C. For each student, write an equation that gives the relationship between the time and the distance walked. Let d represent the distance in meters and t represent the time in seconds. How does the walking rate affect the equations?

Assignment Choices

ACE questions 1–5, 7–9, and unassigned choices from earlier problems

Answers to Problem 2.2

A. See page 34l.

B. See page 34m.

C. Terry: $d = t$, Jade: $d = 2t$, Jerome: $d = 2.5t$; As the walking rate increases, the coefficient of t increases.

■ **Problem 2.2 Follow-Up**

While reading a sports magazine, Abby finds the following time and distance data for an athlete in an Olympic race. She wonders whether the data represent a linear relationship. Abby knows that if the relationship is linear, the data will lie on a straight line when graphed.

Time (seconds)	Distance (meters)
0	0
1	2
2	4
3	8
4	13
5	17

1. Use the table to determine how the distance changes as the time increases. How can you use this information to predict whether or not the data will lie on a straight line when graphed?

2. Describe the race that might have produced these data.

2.3 Walking for Charity

Ms. Chang's class decides to participate in a walkathon to raise money for a local hospital. Each participant in the walkathon must find sponsors to pledge a certain amount of money for each mile the participant walks.

Ms. Chang says that some sponsors might ask the students to suggest a pledge amount. The class wants to agree on how much they will ask for. Leanne says that $1 per mile would be appropriate. Gilberto says that $2 per mile would be better because it would bring in more money. Alana points out that if they ask for too much money, not as many people will want to be sponsors. She suggests that they ask each sponsor for a $5 donation plus 50¢ per mile.

Answers to Problem 2.2 Follow-Up

1. The rate of change between the entries for the distance is not constant; as time increases by 1, distance increases by different amounts. For example, as time goes from 1 to 2 seconds, distance goes from 2 to 4 meters (a change of 2 meters); as time goes from 2 to 3 seconds, distance goes from 4 to 8 meters (a change of 4 meters). The data will not lie in a straight line.

2. Possible answer: The runner started from a motionless position and took a few seconds to pick up speed.

- - - - - - - - -

At a Glance

Grouping: individuals, then small groups

Launch

- Tell the story of the walkathon, and talk about the three pledge plans.

- Have students work individually to make a table and a graph and to write equations.

Explore

- Ask students who are having trouble writing equations to verbalize the relationships first.

- In groups, have students share their answers to the problem.

Summarize

- As a class, talk about how the rate paid per mile shows up in the table, graph, and equations.

- Have groups work on the follow-up, then discuss their answers.

- Save the tables, graphs, and equations for Problem 3.1.

Assignment Choices

ACE questions 6, 18–20, and unassigned choices from earlier problems

Problem 2.3

In this problem, we will refer to Leanne, Gilberto, and Alana's suggestions as pledge plans.

A. 1. Make a table showing the amount of money a sponsor would owe under each pledge plan if a student walked distances between 0 and 10 miles.

    2. Graph the three pledge plans on the same coordinate axes. Use a different color for each plan.

    3. For each pledge plan, write an equation that can be used to calculate the amount of money a sponsor owes, given the total distance the student walks.

B. What effect does increasing the amount pledged per mile have on the table? On the graph? On the equation?

C. If a student walks 8 miles in the walkathon, how much would a sponsor owe under each pledge plan? Explain how you got your answer.

D. For a sponsor to owe a student $10, how many miles would the student have to walk under each pledge plan? Explain how you got your answer.

E. Alana suggested that each sponsor make a $5 donation and then pledge 50¢ per mile. How is this fixed $5 donation represented in the table? In the graph? In the equation?

■ **Problem 2.3 Follow-Up**

1. a. On the graph of a pledge plan, the point (2, 6) means that a student who walks 2 miles earns $6 from each sponsor. On which of the graphs is the point (2, 6)?

    b. Find a point on each graph, and describe what the coordinates of the point mean in the context of the walkathon.

2. a. Write an equation for a pledge plan whose graph is a steeper line than any of the lines you graphed in the problem. Check your equation by graphing it on the coordinate axes with the other three lines.

    b. Write an equation for a pledge plan whose graph is less steep than any of the lines you graphed in the problem. Check your equation by graphing it on the coordinate axes with the other lines.

Answers to Problem 2.3

See page 34m.

Answers to Problem 2.3 Follow-Up

1. a. The point (2, 6) is on Alana's graph.

    b. Possible answer: The point (0, 5) lies on Alana's graph and means that if a student entered the walkathon but did not walk, each of that student's sponsors would still owe $5. The point (8, 16) lies on Gilberto's graph and means that if a student walks 8 miles, each sponsor owes $16. The point (8, 8) is on Leanne's graph and means that if a student walks 8 miles, each sponsor owes $8.

2. See page 34n.

2.4 Walking to Win

In Mr. Goldberg's gym class, Emile finds out that his walking rate is 2.5 meters per second. When he gets home from school, he times his little brother Henri, as Henri walks 100 meters. He figures out that Henri's walking rate is 1 meter per second.

Henri challenges Emile to a walking race. Because Emile's walking rate is faster, Emile gives Henri a 45-meter head start.

Problem 2.4

Emile knows his brother would enjoy winning the race, but he does not want to make the race so short that it is obvious his brother will win.

What would be a good distance to make the race so that Henri will win in a close race? Describe your strategy, and give evidence to support your answer.

■ Problem 2.4 Follow-Up

What would be a good distance to choose if Emile wants to beat his brother but wants the race to be close? Explain.

At a Glance

**Grouping:
groups of 3 or 4**

Launch

- Read the story of the boys' walking rates and their race.

- Challenge the class to decide on both the head start and the length of the race. *(optional)*

Explore

- Circulate as groups work, asking them to explain their work.

- Tell groups to reach a consensus about an answer or to be prepared to explain why more than one answer is reasonable.

Summarize

- Discuss the groups' strategies for determining the length of the race.

- Explore the follow-up as part of the summary.

Answer to Problem 2.4

The race should be less than 75 meters long; thus, the race should last less than 30 seconds. (See the summary for possible strategies for determining this distance.)

Answer to Problem 2.4 Follow-Up

A race length of slightly longer than 75 meters would mean that Emile would win but just barely.

Assignment Choices

ACE questions 10–12 and unassigned choices from earlier problems

Crossing the Line

At a Glance

Grouping: individuals, then small groups

Launch

■ Talk with the class about using tables, graphs, and equations to answer the questions in Problem 2.4.

■ Have students work individually to make a table and a graph and to write equations, then have them share answers in groups.

Explore

■ After groups finish the problem, have them work on the follow-up.

Summarize

■ Let groups share their representations.

■ Make sure the class understands how a pair of values is represented in a table, a graph, and an equation.

■ Talk about the follow-up, which informally introduces the concepts of slope and *y*-intercept.

In Problem 2.4, there are many strategies you can use to determine a good distance for the race. Some strategies are more efficient or useful than others. Here are three powerful ways to tackle the problem:

1. Make a table showing time and distance data for both brothers.

2. On the same set of axes, graph time and distance data for both brothers.

3. Write an equation for each brother showing the relationship between the time and the distance from the starting line.

Problem 2.5

Use the information from Problem 2.4.

A. 1. Make a table showing the distance each brother is from the starting line at several different times during the first 40 seconds.

2. On the same set of axes, graph the time and the distance from the starting line for both brothers.

3. Write an equation for each brother showing the relationship between the time and the distance from the starting line.

B. How far from the starting line will Emile overtake Henri? Explain how you can use the table and the graph to answer this question.

C. After how many seconds will Emile overtake Henri? Explain how you can use the table and the graph to answer this question.

 Problem 2.5 Follow-Up

1. After 3 seconds, who will be ahead? By how much?

2. How far will Henri be from the starting line when Emile has walked 10 meters?

3. a. Which graph is steeper?

b. How can you determine which of two lines will be steeper from their tables? From their equations?

4. Explain how you can use the table, the graph, and the equations to determine how far from the starting line each brother will be after 5 minutes.

5. a. At what points do Emile's and Henri's graphs cross the *y*-axis? What do these points mean in terms of the race?

b. How can you predict where a graph will cross the *y*-axis from a table? From an equation?

Assignment Choices

ACE questions 13, 21, 22, and unassigned choices from earlier problems

Assessment

It is appropriate to use the check-up after this problem.

Answers to Problem 2.5

See page 34n.

Answers to Problem 2.5 Follow-Up

1. Henri will be ahead by 48 − 7.5 = 40.5 m.

2. It takes Emile 4 s to walk 10 m. At that time, Henri will be 49 m from the starting line.

3. a. Emile's graph is steeper.

   b. The greater the rate, or the faster someone walks, the steeper the line will be. From a table, look at how much the variable on the vertical axis is changing in relation to the variable on the horizontal axis. From the equation, look at the walking rate, which is multiplied by the time.

6. Emile's friend Yvette joins the race. Yvette has a head start of 20 meters and walks at 2 meters per second.

   a. Copy and complete the table below to show Yvette's distance from the starting line for 0 to 7 seconds.

Time (seconds)	Distance (meters)
0	20
1	
2	
3	
4	
5	
6	
7	

   b. Which of the following equations gives the relationship between Yvette's distance from the starting line, d, and the time, t?

   i. $d = 20 + 2t$

   ii. $d = 2 + 20$

   iii. $d = 20t + 2$

   iv. $d = 20 + t$

   v.   none of the above

4. The table would need to be continued to 300 s and the distance calculated at that point. The graph would need to be extended to 300 s and the distance at that point read from the vertical axis. To use the equations, substitute 300 for t and solve for d.

5. a. Emile's graph crosses the y-axis at 0; Henri's crosses at 45. These values are the meters from the starting line at the point each boy began the race.

   b. From a table, you can tell where the graph will cross the y-axis by looking at when the variable on the horizontal axis is 0. From an equation, you can look at the number that is added to the term containing time.

6. a. See page 34o.

   b. equation i, $d = 20 + 2t$

Answers

Applications

1a. José: 15 ÷ 3 = 5 mph, Mario: 21 ÷ 3 = 7 mph, Melanie: 27 ÷ 3 = 9 mph

1b. José: 7 × 5 = 35 mi, Mario: 7 × 7 = 49 mi, Melanie: 7 × 9 = 63 mi

2a. See below right.

2b. José: about 33 mi, Mario: about 46 mi, Melanie: about 59 mi

2c. José: 14 h, Mario: 10 h, Melanie: about 7.8 h

2d. The faster the cyclist, the steeper the graph.

3a. José: $d = 5t$, Mario: $d = 7t$, Melanie: $d = 9t$

3b. José: 32.5 mi, Mario: 45.5 mi, Melanie: 58.5 mi

3c. The rate shows up in the equation as the number being multiplied by t.

Applications • Connections • Extensions

As you work on these ACE questions, use your calculator whenever you need it.

Applications

In 1–3, use the following information: José, Mario, and Melanie went on a weeklong cycling trip. The table below gives the distance each person traveled for the first 3 hours of the trip. The table shows only the time when the riders were actually biking, not when they stopped to rest, eat, and so on.

Cycling time (hours)	Distance (miles)		
	José	Mario	Melanie
0	0	0	0
1	5	7	9
2	10	14	18
3	15	21	27

1. **a.** How fast did each person travel for the first 3 hours? Explain how you got your answer.

    b. Assume that each person continued at this rate. Find the distance each person traveled in 7 hours.

2. **a.** Graph the time and distance data for all three riders on the same coordinate axes.

    b. Use the graphs to find the distance each person traveled in $6\frac{1}{2}$ hours.

    c. Use the graphs to find the time it took each person to travel 70 miles.

    d. How does the rate at which each person rides affect the graphs?

3. **a.** For each rider, write an equation that can be used to calculate the distance traveled after a given number of hours.

    b. Use your equations from part a to calculate the distance each person traveled in $6\frac{1}{2}$ hours.

    c. How does a person's biking rate show up in his or her equation?

2a.

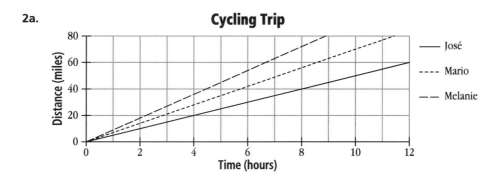

4. Mike was on the bike trip with José, Mario, and Melanie (from questions 1–3). He made the following table of the distances he traveled during day 1 of the trip.

Time (hours)	Distance (miles)
0	0
1	6.5
2	13
3	19.5
4	26
5	32.5
6	39

a. Assume Mike continued riding at this rate for the entire bike trip. Write an equation for the distance Mike traveled after t hours.

b. Sketch a graph of the equation.

c. When you made your graph, how did you choose the range of values for the time axis? For the distance axis?

d. How can you find the distance Mike traveled in 7 hours and in $9\frac{1}{2}$ hours, using the table? The graph? The equation?

e. How can you find the number of hours it took Mike to travel 100 miles and 237 miles, using the table? The graph? The equation?

f. For parts d and e, give the advantages and disadvantages of using each form of representation—a table, a graph, and an equation—to find the answers.

g. Compare the rate at which Mike rides with the rates at which José, Mario, and Melanie ride. Who rides the fastest? How can you determine this from the tables? From the graphs? From the equations?

4b.
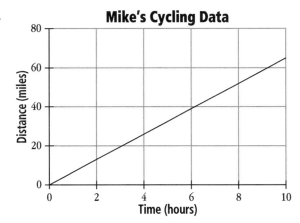

4a. $d = 6.5t$

4b. See below left.

4c. Answers will vary. Students should support their choices.

4d. The table could be extended to show 7 h and $9\frac{1}{2}$ h. On the graph, the distances at these points may be approximated. In the equation, the values of 7 h and $9\frac{1}{2}$ h could be substituted for t, which gives the answers 45.5 mi and 61.75 mi.

4e. The table could be extended to show 100 mi and 237 mi. On the graph, the times at these points may be approximated. In the equation, the values of 100 mi and 237 mi can be substituted for d, which gives the approximate answers 15.4 h and 36.5 h.

4f. Possible answer: If the value is already showing, the table or graph would be easy to use. The equations are easier to use for values that are far from those shown on the table or graph.

4g. In decreasing order, the bikers' speeds are Melanie's, Mario's, Mike's, and José's. In the tables this can be found by comparing the distance biked after 1 hour or by finding the difference between any two consecutive distances (for times in increments of 1 hour). In the graphs, the steepness of the line relays this information. In the equations, the bikers' rates can be compared by noting the number by which t is multiplied.

5a. 7.5 mph

5b. It would still go through the point (0, 0) but would be steeper than Mike's graph.

5c. In decreasing order of steepness, the lines would be Melanie's, Alicia's, Mario's, and José's.

6a. One Size: $c = 4t$, You Draw It: $c = 75 + 3t$ (where c is the cost and t is the number of T-shirts)

6b. See below right.

6c. If fewer than 75 T-shirts are ordered, One Size has the better offer. If more than 75 are ordered, You Draw It has the better offer. This is where the lines cross on the graph; after this point, the line for One Size is higher than the line for You Draw It.

6d. The costs are equal at 75 T-shirts. This is where the graphs cross.

---

5. Alicia was also on the bike trip. The distance she traveled in t hours is represented by this equation:

$$d = 7.5t$$

a. At what rate did Alicia travel?

b. If the graph of Alicia's distance and time were put on the same set of axes as Mike's graph, where would it be located in relationship to Mike's graph? Describe the location without actually making the graph.

c. If the graph of Alicia's distance and time were put on the same set of axes as José's, Mario's, and Melanie's graphs, where would it be located in relationship to the other graphs? Describe the location without actually making the graph.

6. The students in Ms. Chang's class decide to order T-shirts that advertise the walkathon. Miguel obtains two different quotes for the costs for the shirts.

One Size Fits All charges $4 per shirt.
You Draw It/We Print It charges $75 plus $3 per shirt.

a. For each company, write an equation Miguel could use to calculate the cost for any number of shirts.

b. On the same set of axes, graph both equations from part a.

c. Which company do you think the class should buy shirts from? What factors influenced your decision?

d. For what number of T-shirts is the cost the same for both companies? Explain how you got your answer.

26 Moving Straight Ahead

6b.

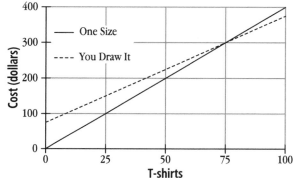

Walkathon T-Shirts

26 Investigation 2

In 7–9, refer to tables a–c.

a.

x	y
−2	3
−1	3
0	3
1	3
2	3
3	3

b.

x	y
−3	9
−2	4
−1	1
0	0
1	1
2	4

c.

x	y
0	0
2	−4
3	−8
4	−12
8	−16

7. How are the patterns in tables a–c similar? How are they different?

8. Make a graph of the data in each table.

9. Which tables represent a linear relationship? Explain how you decided.

10. The equation $C = 10 + 2n$ represents the cost in dollars, C, for n painter's caps advertising the walkathon. Which pair of values could represent a number of caps and the cost for that number of caps, (n, C)? Explain your answer.

(0, 10)   (7, 24)   (15, 30)

11. The equation $d = 3.5t + 50$ represents the distance in meters, d, that a cyclist is from his home after t seconds. Which pair of values represents a point on the graph of this equation? Explain your answer.

(10, 85)   (0, 0)   (3, 60.5)

---

7. See page 34o.

8. See below left.

9. Only table a represents a linear relationship. There is a constant change in y for consecutive values of x, and the graph of table a is the only straight line.

10. Points (0, 10) and (7, 24) both represent a number of caps and their cost. We can see this by substituting the values into the equation: $10 = 10 + 2(0)$ and $24 = 10 + 2(7)$.

11. Points (10, 85) and (3, 60.5) both represent a point on the graph. We can see this by substituting: $85 = 3.5(10) + 50$ and $60.5 = 3.5(3) + 50$.

8.

Table a

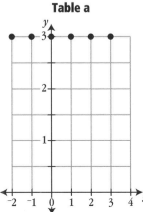

Table b

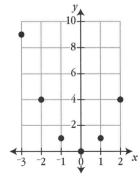

Table c

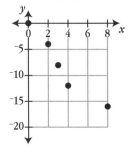

12a. The situation is like the race between Henri and Emile in that the question asks when the person traveling at the greater rate will catch up to the other person. In both cases, the person traveling at the slower rate has a head start. In this situation, the head start is given as a time rather than as a distance. (Note: This distinction is blurred on the graph, because the y-intercept indicates the head start as a distance as well as a time.)

12b. after 4 min

12c. 1000 ft from Tara's house

12d. The intersection of Tara's graph at 500 means that when Ingrid started running, Tara was 500 ft ahead of her. The intersection of Ingrid's line at 0 means that Ingrid was at Tara's house when she started running.

12e. See page 34o.

12f. Possible answer: It will continue as a single line.

12. Ingrid stops at Tara's house on her way to school. Tara's mother says that Tara left 4 minutes ago. Ingrid leaves Tara's house, running to catch up with Tara. The graph below shows the distance each girl is from Tara's house, starting from the time Ingrid leaves Tara's house.

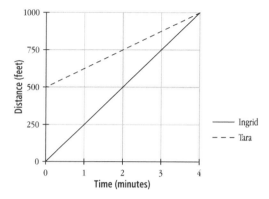

a. In what way is this situation like the race between Henri and Emile? In what way is it different?

b. After how many minutes does Ingrid catch up with Tara?

c. How far from Tara's house does Ingrid catch up with Tara?

d. Each graph intersects the distance axis (the y-axis). What information do the points of intersection give about the problem?

e. Which line is steeper? How can you tell from the graph? How is the steepness of each line related to the rate at which the person travels?

f. What do you think the graphs would look like if we extended them to show distance and time after the girls meet?

13. The organizers of the walkathon want to have brochures printed to advertise the event. They get cost estimates from two printing companies. The costs are given by the equations

Company A: $C = 15 + 0.10n$
Company B: $C = 0.25n$

where C is the cost in dollars and n is the number of brochures.

a. Graph both equations on the same set of axes.

b. For what number of brochures is the cost the same for both companies?

c. The organizers have $65 to spend on brochures. How many brochures can they have printed if they use company A? If they use company B? Describe the method you used to get your answers.

d. At what point does each graph intersect the vertical axis? What information does each of these points give?

e. Explain what the numbers 15 and 0.10 represent in the equation for company A.

f. Explain what the number 0.25 represents in the equation for company B.

Connections

14. The 1996 Olympic gold medal winner for the 20-kilometer walk was Jefferson Perez from Ecuador. His time was 1 hour, 20 minutes, 7 seconds. Perez's time was not good enough to beat the Olympic record set in 1988 by Josef Pribilinec from Czechoslovakia. Pribilinec's record for the 20-kilometer walk was 1 hour, 19 minutes, 57 seconds. What was the walking rate of each person?

Josef Pribilinec

13a.

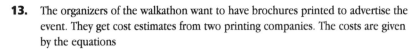

13a. See below left.

13b. 100 brochures

13c. company A: 500 brochures, company B: 260 brochures; Students may continue the graph to obtain these answers, or they may solve the equations for n.

13d. The graph for company A intersects the vertical axis at 15, which represents the initial $15 cost for getting brochures printed. The graph for company B intersects the vertical axis at 0, which means there is no initial cost added to an order for brochures.

13e. The 15 represents the initial cost that company A charges for any order, and the 0.10 represents the amount charged for each brochure printed.

13f. The 0.25 is the rate company B charges to print one brochure. (Note: The fact that 0.25 is greater than 0.10 explains why the graph is steeper. A higher cost per brochure means that total cost increases faster.)

Connections

14. *Perez:* 1 h 20 min 7 s = 4807 s, 20 km = 20,000 m, and 20,000 m ÷ 4807 s = 4.16 m/s (or 14.98 kph); *Pribilinec:* 1 h 19 min 57 s = 4797 s; 20,000 m ÷ 4797 s = 4.17 m/s (or 15.01 kph)

15. 13 h 35 min 18 s = 13.59 h, and 363.1 ÷ 13.59 = 26.72 mph (or 0.45 mi/min or 0.0074 mi/s)

16. 3569 ÷ 24.547 = 145.39 h

17a. 11 min 59.36 s = 719.36 s, and 3000 ÷ 719.36 = 4.17 m/s

17b. 11 min 51.26 s = 711.26 s, and 3000 ÷ 711.26 = 4.22 m/s; Saxby walked 0.05 m/s faster.

18. See page 34o.

15. The longest one-day bike race goes from Bordeaux, France, to Paris, France. The record for this race was set in 1981 by Herman van Springel of Belgium. He finished the 363.1-mile race in 13 hours, 35 minutes, 18 seconds. What was Springel's average speed for the race?

16. The longest human-powered sporting event is the Tour de France cycling race. The record average speed for this race is 24.547 miles per hour, which was obtained by Miguel Indurain of Spain in 1992. If the race is 3569 miles long, how long did it take Indurain to complete the race?

17. In 1990, Beate Anders of East Germany set the women's world record for the 3000-meter walk. She completed the race in 11 minutes, 59.36 seconds.

  a. What was Anders' average walking speed?

  b. In 1991, Kerry Ann Saxby of Australia beat Anders' record. She completed the 3000-meter walk in 11 minutes, 51.26 seconds. How much faster did Saxby walk than Anders?

18. a. Generate a table and a graph for $y = 5x - 2$. Look back at the graphs you made in this investigation. How is the graph of this equation different from the other graphs you made?

  b. Generate a table and a graph for $y = {}^-2x + 3$. How is the graph different from the other graphs you made in this investigation?

  c. Generate a table and write an equation for the graph below. How is this graph different from the other graphs you made in this investigation?

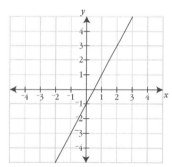

19. The table below shows the amount of orange juice concentrate and water needed to make a given number of batches of juice.

Batches of juice (b)	Concentrate (c)	Water (w)	Juice (j)
1	2 cups	3 cups	5 cups
2	4 cups	6 cups	10 cups
3	6 cups	9 cups	15 cups

a. The relationship between the number of batches of juice and the number of cups of concentrate is linear. The equation for this relationship is $c = 2b$. Are there other linear relationships in this table? Make graphs or write equations for the linear relationships you find.

b. A different recipe calls for 3 cups of concentrate and 5 cups of water. Which recipe gives the more "orangey" drink? Explain how you found your answer.

20. The tables below give information about two fruit punch recipes. Each table shows the number of cups of orange juice, pineapple juice, and soda water needed for different quantities of punch. The relationship between cups of orange juice and cups of pineapple juice is linear, and the relationship between cups of orange juice and cups of soda water is linear.

Recipe 1

j	p	s
1		
2	6	3
3		
4	12	6
5		
6		

Recipe 2

j	p	s
1		
2		
3	8	6
4		
5		
6	16	12

a. Shannon made recipe 1, using 6 cups of orange juice. How many cups of pineapple juice and how many cups of soda water did she use?

b. Patrick made recipe 2, using 4 cups of orange juice. How many cups of pineapple juice and how many cups of soda water did he use?

19a. Possible answer: $w = 3b$, $j = 5b$ (Note: In addition, $w = \frac{3}{2}c$, $j = \frac{5}{2}c$, $j = \frac{5}{3}w$, $b = \frac{1}{3}w$, $b = \frac{1}{5}j$, $b = \frac{1}{2}c$; students are not as likely to see these relationships unless they graph *all* relationships between pairs of variables.)

19b. Possible answer: The strength of the juice depends on the rate of concentrate to water. This can be seen from the relationship between amount of water and amount of concentrate. In the first recipe, $w = \frac{3}{2}c$; in the second, $w = \frac{5}{3}c$. Since $\frac{5}{3}$ is greater than $\frac{3}{2}$, the proportion of water is greater in the second recipe. The first recipe will have a stronger flavor.

20a. Recipe 1 requires 3 c of pineapple juice and $1\frac{1}{2}$ c of soda water for 1 c of orange juice. For 6 c of orange juice, Shannon used 18 c of pineapple juice and 9 c of soda water.

20b. For recipe 2, $p = \frac{8}{3}j$ and $s = 2j$. For 4 c of orange juice, Patrick used $\frac{32}{3} = 10\frac{2}{3}$ c of pineapple juice and 8 c of soda water.

21a. See page 34p.

21b. See graph below right. (Note: Notice that the graph has time on the horizontal axis and distance on the vertical axis. Students are accustomed to thinking of distance as depending on the time. The equations in part c show this as well. However, this table is set up in reverse, in a way, as students are asked to find the time given the distance. Some students may think of time as dependent on distance and put time on the vertical axis. The related equations are $\frac{d}{270} = t$ and $\frac{d}{330} = t$, and the graph will show the distance as x and the time as y.)

21c. NY to SF: $d = 270t$; SF to NY: $d = 330t$

21d. against the wind: $5000 \div 270 = 18.52$ h; with the wind: $5000 \div 330 = 15.15$ h

Extensions

21. Wind can affect the speed of an airplane. Suppose a plane is making a round-trip from New York City to San Francisco. The plane has a cruising speed of 300 miles per hour. The wind is blowing from west to east at 30 miles per hour. When the plane flies into (in the opposite direction of) the wind, its speed decreases by 30 miles per hour. When the plane flies with (in the same direction as) the wind, its speed increases by 30 miles per hour. The distance between New York City and San Francisco is 3000 miles.

a. Make a table that shows the total time the plane has traveled after each 200-mile interval on its trip from New York City to San Francisco and back.

Distance (miles)	NYC to SF time (hours)	SF to NYC time (hours)
0		
200		
400		
600		
.		
.		
.		

b. On the same set of axes, make graphs of time and distance data for travel in both directions.

c. For each direction, write an equation for the distance, d, traveled in t hours.

d. How long would it take this plane to fly 5000 miles against a 30-mile-per-hour wind? With a 30-mile-per-hour wind? Explain how you found your answers.

21b.

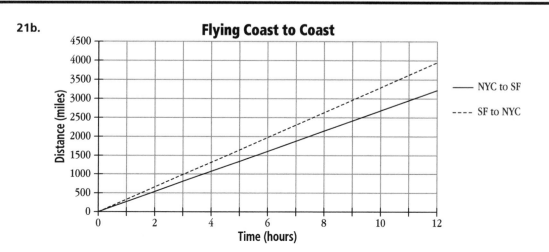

Flying Coast to Coast

— NYC to SF

---- SF to NYC

22. The table below shows the population of four cities for the past eight years.

Year	Population			
	Deep Valley	Nowhere	Swampville	Mount Silicon
0 (Start)	1000	1000	1000	1000
1	1500	900	1500	2000
2	2000	800	2500	4000
3	2500	750	3000	8000
4	3000	700	5000	16,000
5	3500	725	3000	32,000
6	4000	900	2500	64,000
7	4500	1500	1500	128,000
8	5000	1700	1000	256,000

a. Describe how the population of each city changed over the eight years.

b. Graph the data for each city. Describe how you selected ranges of values for the horizontal and vertical axes.

c. What are the advantages of each representation?

22a. For Deep Valley, as the number of years increased, the population increased at a constant rate. Nowhere's population gradually decreased at a nonconstant rate and then made a quick increase. Swampville's population increased at a nonconstant rate until the fourth year, then decreased at the same rate it had increased. Mount Silicon's population doubled each year.

22b. See page 34q.

22c. Possible answer: The tables may be more appropriate if you wanted to know the precise population of a city at a certain time. The graphs give a picture of the population over time at a quick glance, and they show overall trends better than tables do.

Possible Answers

1. When a relationship is linear, the table will show constant differences in consecutive values of the dependent variable for constant increments in the independent variable. In the equation, this constant rate of change between the two variables is the coefficient of the independent variable.

2. See page 34q.

3. In the graphs, the line that rises more steeply represents the relationship with the greater rate. In the table, the greater the difference in the dependent variable per unit change in the independent variable, the greater the rate. In the equation, the greater the number multiplying the independent variable, the greater the rate.

4. See page 34q.

(Note: In some classes, students use the words *independent* and *dependent* from the beginning and find them useful to help make decisions about variables and how they are related. Some students may not use this terminology, instead referring to the independent and dependent variables as the "first" and "second" variables, or they may use examples. If you continue to use the language and to stress what it means, students will pick it up over time.)

Mathematical Reflections

In this investigation, you learned how to recognize a linear relationship from a table, and you explored the effect that changing the rate has on the table, graph, and equation of a linear relationship. These questions will help you summarize what you have learned:

1 How can you decide whether a relationship is linear by looking at its table or its equation?

2 In the situations you explored, how did the rate—such as the meters per second a student walks or the dollars per mile a sponsor pledges—show up in the table, the graph, and the equation of a linear relationship?

3 How can you compare the rates for two linear relationships by looking at their graphs? Their tables? Their equations?

4 When might you use a graph to answer a question about a linear relationship? When might you use a table? When might you use an equation?

Think about your answers to these questions, discuss your ideas with other students and your teacher, and then write a summary of your findings in your journal.

Tips for the Linguistically Diverse Classroom

Original Rebus The Original Rebus technique is described in detail in *Getting to Know Connected Mathematics*. Students make a copy of the text before it is discussed. During the discussion, they generate their own rebuses for words they do not understand; the words are made comprehensible through pictures, objects, or demonstrations. Example: Question 4—Key words for which students might make rebuses are *graph* (a grid with *x*- and *y*-axes), *linear relationship* (two points on a grid connected by a straight line), *table* (outline of a table), *equation* ($y = mx + b$).

TEACHING THE INVESTIGATION

2.1 • Walking to the Yogurt Shop

In Investigation 1, students explored some situations that could be modeled by linear relationships; however, none of the characteristics of a linear relationship were defined. In this problem, students consider the impact of different rates on the time taken to travel a set distance. This problem allows precise tables and graphs to be made to represent the relationships and thus makes the features characteristic of linear relationships more apparent. However, the problem is posed in an open-ended fashion, which allows you to see what sense your students are making of rate situations. This sets the stage for the rest of the investigation and, in particular, for Problem 2.2, in which students explore the same data in more depth.

Launch

Pose the problem, and let students approach it using whatever methods make sense to them. This problem should not take very long. Having students work in groups of two to four will allow you to see which students are asking themselves good questions and who needs a bit of guidance.

Explore

It is important to let students make sense of the problem without imposing a method for their exploration. However, you may want to ask questions that remind students of the techniques they used in the experiments to make sense of the data. One thing students might need reminding of is to look at the data and to think about what the relationships might be *before* doing more in-depth analysis.

> Before you begin, think about these questions: Which student will get to the frozen yogurt shop first? Where will Terry be when Jade reaches the yogurt shop?

Challenge students to answer these questions by just thinking about the rates at which the three students walk.

As groups work, ask those who finish quickly to write some additional questions that can be answered about the situation. These can be shared during the summary.

Summarize

Let students discuss their strategies for solving the problem. Some may have used strategies from the *Comparing and Scaling* unit to write equivalent ratios or rates; some may have used tables. Others may reason about the problem; for example:

■ "If the distance is 750 meters, it will take Jade—who walks 2 meters per second— $750 \div 2 = 375$ seconds or 6.25 minutes. Similarly, Terry will take 12.5 minutes, and Jerome will take 5 minutes. So Terry will arrive at the frozen yogurt shop last—7.5 minutes behind Jerome and 6.25 minutes behind Jade."

- "Jerome is walking away from Jade at a rate of 0.5 meters per second. In 1 minute, he will have walked $0.5 \times 60 = 30$ meters farther."

Later in the unit, this kind of thinking will be used to develop a method for solving equations algebraically, but there is no need to insist on formal methods at this time.

Discuss the follow-up questions as part of the summary. Some students will say the relationships are linear; some may even make quick sketches of the data to see whether the points for each student's walking rate lie in a straight line. Most will probably not know whether the relationships involved are linear—again, as this will be studied in depth in this unit, there's no need to push for this understanding at this time. Simply asking the questions helps to set the scene for the rest of the unit.

Use the summary to lead into the launch of Problem 2.2.

> In the next few problems, we will develop ways to determine whether a relationship is linear—and we will discover why linear relationships are important.

2.2 • Changing the Walking Rate

In this reprise of Problem 2.1, students examine the effect of different rates on graphs, tables, and equations, and consider the question of linearity more directly.

Launch

Launch this problem from the summary of Problem 2.1.

> Suppose you know the rate at which you walk. If you increase your walking rate, you will cover more distance in a given time. In other words, if you walk faster, it will take less time to walk a certain distance.
>
> Suppose you have made a table, a graph, and an equation of your distance over time at your slower walking rate. What effect will increasing your walking rate have on the table, the graph, and the equation?
>
> In this problem, you will investigate similar questions by looking again at Terry's, Jade's, and Jerome's walking rates. You will make a table, create a graph, and write an equation for each walker. Then, you will examine these to see what effects the walking rate has on each form of representation.

In this situation, the distance traveled *depends* on the time. Ask the class which axis should represent time. In this type of situation, the horizontal axis is usually used to represent time (the independent variable in this case), and the vertical axis is usually used to represent distance (the dependent variable).

Explore

Have students individually make a table and a graph and write equations. If a student is having trouble getting started, pair that student temporarily with another who seems to be on target. Then, have students work in groups of two to four to compare their data and to discuss the effects on each representation of changing the rate.

Assign the follow-up to be done in the groups. The follow-up raises the question of whether *every* situation is linear. As you circulate, you might ask groups to make a data table that does not represent a linear situation, a graph that does not represent a linear situation, and even an equation that is not linear. Writing an equation that is nonlinear is more difficult for students than making a table or a graph showing nonlinear data, but asking them to try will get them thinking about the idea. (In the summary, you can talk about this issue as a class; see the suggestion below.)

Summarize

Discuss each type of representation. Ask questions that help students notice that for each unit change in time, there is a constant change in the distance walked by Terry, Jade, and Jerome. Help the class explore these constant rates of change in the three representations.

Constant rate of change in a table: It may be a bit difficult for students to recognize the effect that different walking rates have on a table. Ask questions to lead them to these discoveries.

> Jade walks at 2 meters per second. As the number of seconds increases from 1 to 2, how does the distance change? *(The distance changes by 2 meters.)*
>
> If the time increases by 1 second, does the distance Jade walks always increase by 2 meters? *(yes)*

Ask the class to indicate where this is shown in the table. (The entries in the table for Jade's distance increase by 2 for each 1 second. This is what *2 meters per second* means.)

Time	Distance (meters)		
(seconds)	Terry	Jade	Jerome
0	0	0	0
1	1	2	2.5
2	2	4	5
3	3	6	7.5

> If the time increases by 2 seconds, what is the change in the distance Jade walks? *(4 meters)*

Have the class illustrate this answer using the table. (A change from 1 second to 3 seconds produces a change from 2 meters to 6 meters, or 4 meters, in the distance Jade walks.)

Constant rate of change in a graph: It should be fairly easy for the class to recognize the effect that different walking rates have on a graph: the steepness of the lines are different. Some students may say that the line "goes up faster"; such intuitive ideas are the objective of the unit at this time. Ask questions to extend the class's thinking about this effect.

> What would the graph look like if someone walked 3 meters per second? 5 meters per second? $1\frac{1}{2}$ meters per second? $\frac{1}{2}$ meter per second?
>
> How would each of these walking rates affect the table? How would each of these walking rates affect the equation?

Constant rate of change in equations: Students may be able to recognize the effect that different walking rates have on the equation $d = \text{rate} \times \text{time}$ or, in symbolic form, $d = rt$. The rate, r, is the coefficient of t; it is the number by which the variable time is multiplied. The word *coefficient* is defined in the next investigation; at this point, students will say it is the rate at which people walk and the number that time is multiplied by to get the distance walked.

To pull together what students have discovered about the three representations, ask questions about using tables, graphs, or equations to find information.

> How could you use the table to find the distance a particular student walks in 2 minutes? The time it takes to walk 100 meters? How could you use the graphs? How could you use the equations?

Students often hold the idea that, in a table, each value for x must be exactly 1 greater. It is helpful to raise this issue explicitly. As a class, look at tables such as those shown below to expand students' understanding of this representation.

x	y
5	18
10	33
15	48
20	63

x	y
0	0
3	12
5	20
8	32
10	40

In the first table, we see that $33 - 18 = 15$, $48 - 33 = 15$, and $63 - 48 = 15$. This means that for each change of 5 in x, there is a change of 15 in y. For a change of 1 in x, there must be a corresponding change of $15 \div 5 = 3$ in y.

In the second table, changes in x are not evenly spaced, so we must be more careful. We see that $12 - 0 = 12$. So, for a change of 3 in x, there is a change of 12 in y. If the relationship between x and y is linear, a change in x of 1 should give a change in y of 4. Checking this relationship with other data in the table shows that this indeed is the relationship: a change of 1 in x is related to a change of 4 in y. For example, from (8, 32) to (10, 40), the change in x is $10 - 8 = 2$ and the change in y is $40 - 32 = 8$.

To fully understand linear relationships, students must also see examples of linear and nonlinear situations. The follow-up questions pose a situation that is not linear. It is important to discuss this example in class and compare it to linear situations.

Put the table from the follow-up on the board or overhead.

Time (seconds)	Distance (meters)
0	0
1	2
2	4
3	8
4	13
5	17

Do these data represent a straight line? How can we tell?

Students may suggest sketching a graph. If the data are graphed, they will not give a straight line.

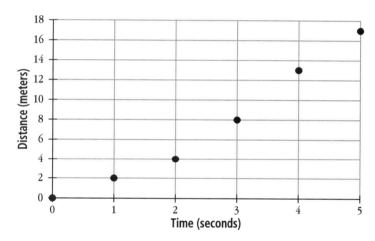

If none of the students uses the data directly from the table to argue that they do not represent a straight line, ask:

How can we use the *table* to prove that this is not a linear relationship? *(As the time increases 1 unit, there is not a constant increase in the distance. From 0 seconds to 1 second, the distance increases 2 meters; from 2 to 3 seconds, the distance increases 4 meters.)*

Help the class to generalize what they have discovered.

How can we use a graph to determine whether a set of data is linear? *(The graph will be a straight line.)* How can we use a table? *(There will be a constant rate of change between the variables.)* How can we use an equation?

Most students will not be able to answer this last question now. Do not answer the question for them. Instead, ask that they continue to think about it as they work through the next few problems. It is unlikely that all students will understand the idea of a constant rate of change at this time; this is fine, as they will also work on this concept throughout the unit.

Some teachers present another example of nonlinearity, such as that shown in the table below, in addition to the one posed in the follow-up.

Time (seconds)	Distance (meters)
1	2
2	4
3	8
4	16
5	32

This relationship is similar to the ones students have worked on previously in that it is possible to predict the next entry but the rate of change is not constant. That is, a constant number is not added to an entry to get the next entry. In fact, many students can offer a rule that would generate this table (such as that "you get the next distance by doubling the one before or by multiplying by 2"). When the data points are graphed, it is clear that there is a predictable relationship but that the data do not lie on a straight line. Some students may see that the relationship is 2^n, but don't expect this of everyone. The power of this example is to show that there are "nice" relationships that are not linear.

Another nonlinear example that even more students can find the rule for ($y = x^2$) is shown in the table below.

Time (seconds)	Distance (meters)
1	1
2	4
3	9
4	16
5	25

2.3 • Walking for Charity

This problem gives students an opportunity to think about another kind of rate, payment per mile. The focus is again on how different rates affect the various representations—graphs, tables, and equations. This sets the stage for students to begin to see that many situations are governed by a rate and that these situations are recognizable from the related table, graph, or equation. A new idea, a nonzero y-intercept, is introduced in this problem.

Launch

Tell the story of the walkathon, and talk about the pledge plans with the class. Then, ask:

> Are there other things the students might consider in determining the amount of money that potential sponsors would pledge?
>
> Using each of these pledge plans, how can you decide how much to charge for the distance walked?

Have each student individually make a table and a graph and write equations, then collaborate on their conclusions in groups of two or three students.

Explore

As you circulate, ask students how they found their solutions and why they seem reasonable. Look for students who have interesting ways of explaining their thinking, and make sure their ideas are shared in the summary.

Most students will have little problem making the table and the graph; writing the equations may be difficult for some. Encourage students having trouble to first write out each relationship in words. For example, in Leanne's pledge plan, verbalizing that a sponsor will owe $1 for each mile a participant walks is the first step toward being able to state the relationship in symbols: $A = 1d$, where A is the amount of money the sponsor owes and d is the distance (miles walked).

Summarize

The effects of the cost per mile on the representations are similar to the effects of the walking rate in Problem 2.2. Help students to see this similarity. It is important that they see and understand that the mathematical conclusions are the same; only the setting has changed.

> How is the effect of cost per mile similar to the effect of the walking rate in the last problem? *(The cost per mile affects how the cost increases, and the walking rate affects how the distance increases; both are constant rates, and both relationships give straight-line graphs.)*
>
> How do the tables, graphs, and equations from Problem 2.2 compare to the tables, graphs, and equations for this problem?
>
> How can you tell whether a set of data is linear by examining a graph? A table? An equation?

As a class, compare how the effect of the cost per mile shows up in each representation. Continue the conversation until the following ideas have been discussed:

- In the table, it is easy to see that for each constant change in the distance, there is a corresponding constant change in the amount of money a sponsor would owe.

- The graphs are straight lines, and two of them go through the point (0, 0).

- In two of the equations, we just multiply the amount for each mile by the number of miles walked. That is similar to the last problem, in which we multiplied the rate at which people walked by the number of seconds they walked to find out how far they walked. In both cases, we had to multiply. This is true in all the equations, except for Alana's pledge plan, in which we multiply and also have to add a number. (These ideas will be explored in more depth in subsequent problems.)

Now return to the question, asked in the launch, about how this information can be used to decide what to charge each sponsor under each pledge plan.

For part C, discuss, or have students demonstrate, how to use each representation—the table, the graph, and the appropriate equation—to answer the question. Then, ask:

> Which representation seems the most useful for this situation?

In part D, students are asked to reason backward from the amount of money a sponsor would owe to the miles needed to produce that pledge. This is important but may be difficult. Have students explain how they found their solutions. If their explanations are weak, you could explain that you sometimes think about answering questions like this by working backward.

After the summary discussion, assign the follow-up. Talk about the follow-up questions in class to help assess students' understanding about linear situations. The first follow-up question focuses on what information is communicated by a pair of values (a point on the graph) of an equation. The second question explores whether students are beginning to see how the coefficient of x affects the steepness of the related line.

2.4 • Walking to Win

In previous problems, students have compared information from more than one linear relationship to determine the effect of different rates on various representations. In this problem, for the first time, the focus is the point of intersection of two lines (the common solution of two equations).

Launch

Tell the story of the walking race between Emile and his younger brother Henri.

For the Teacher: Letting Henri Win

As an alternative, you could challenge the class to decide on the head start *and* the length of the race. In this open-ended version of the problem, you would supply the rates at which the two brothers walk and explain that Emile wants his brother to win, but barely—he wants the race to appear close. Students must decide what head start Emile should give Henri and how long the race should be.

Allow students to work on the problem in groups of three or four using whatever methods make sense to them. This will give you an opportunity to see what ideas students bring to the problem, and their exploration will serve as a launch to Problem 2.5.

Explore

As you circulate, ask groups to explain their thinking. Put the emphasis on what evidence the group will use to argue for their conclusion. Encourage the groups to listen to each member and to reach a consensus on one answer or to agree that more than one choice is reasonable and be prepared to explain why.

Summarize

Collect the various strategies for establishing a distance for the race. Some of the strategies groups may have used are described below. (Students will make a table and a graph and write equations in Problem 2.5 to represent this situation, so if they haven't tried those representations in this problem, they will encounter them at that time.)

■ Some groups may guess a length for the race, check it, and then adjust the length as necessary. Some may guess a time, check it, and make adjustments.

■ Some groups may generate a table and enter data until they reach a time and a distance that is the same for both boys.

Time (seconds)	Henri's distance from starting line (meters)	Emile's distance from starting line (meters)
0	45	0
10	55	25
20	65	50
30	75	75

Most of the students in one class made a table in units of 1 second and continued to record data until Henri and Emile met; the students choose as the distance for the race the point Henri would reach at just 1 second before the boys would meet.

■ Some groups may graph the situation. The graph of a relationship with the greater rate of change will always overtake the graph of a relationship with the lesser rate of change, even if the latter has a *y*-intercept that is greater than 0 (which is how Henri's head start shows up in the graph).

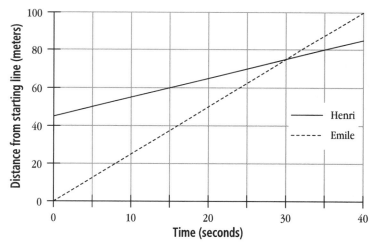

■ A few groups may write equations to represent the situation:

$$d_{\text{Henri}} = t + 45 \qquad\qquad d_{\text{Emile}} = 2.5t$$

Question the class about each suggested length for the race.

How did you determine that the length of the race should be ___?
Why is that length reasonable? By how much will Henri win the race?

Allow students to explain their reasons for each length they suggest. After the class has agreed upon a length or lengths for the race, have them answer the follow-up questions. Then, ask:

How did you determine the length of the race? Why is that length reasonable? By how much will Emile win the race?

For the Teacher: Using Informal Methods

The process of making such decisions is very important. Mathematically, we would probably find the intersection of the two equations and choose a race length slightly less than the length at which Emile overtakes Henri (or slightly greater if we want Emile to win). Students, however, will have more informal ways of thinking about the problem. Their development of these informal ways of thinking will enhance their appreciation and understanding of what more formal mathematical methods can tell them. This transition to using more formal means should proceed slowly.

Use this summary to lead into the launch of Problem 2.5. If someone has created a table, use it in the launch of the next problem.

2.5 • Crossing the Line

Ideas implied in Problem 2.4 are made explicit here. Students will describe the point at which Emile (who has the greater walking rate) overtakes Henri as the point at which the two lines cross on the graph. The time and distance at which this happens can be located on the graph and in the table.

Launch

Launch this problem directly from the summary of Problem 2.4. If your students did not use a table, a graph, or equations in that problem, discuss with them that it is often useful to look at other ways to solve a problem.

Let's see if we can use a table, a graph, or equations to answer the question posed in Problem 2.4. Once you have made your tables, graphs, and equations, you can answer other questions about the race.

Have students individually make a table and a graph and write equations, then discuss in their groups the strategies for using the representations to find information. Have groups then work on the follow-up.

Explore

As you circulate, ask additional questions about features of the graph and the table.

> Why are the two places where the lines cross the *y*-axis different?
>
> What does the vertical (up and down) difference between the lines in the graph tell you?
>
> Can you tell from the table how far Henri is from the starting line after 7 seconds? If so, how?

You may want to ask groups to put their results on blank transparencies or large sheets of paper to facilitate sharing during the summary.

Summarize

Have groups share their representations.

> How can you tell from the table how long the race should be? How can you tell from the graph how long it should be?

In the graph, the distance from the starting line (and the time when Emile overtakes Henri) is the point of intersection (the point where the lines cross). In the table, it is the entry showing the same distance (75 meters) and time (30 seconds) for the two brothers.

Ask questions about various points on the graph and in the table.

> What information does the point (20, 50) represent in the problem? Is this a data point for Henri or for Emile?
>
> How does this point show up in the table? How does it show up in the graph? How does it show up in the equation?

It is fundamentally important that students understand that this is a pair of values from the table for Emile that shows how many meters Emile walks in 20 seconds. From this idea, students can build the understanding that *every pair of values in the table is a point on the graph* and that *every pair of values in the table and on the graph is a pair of values that fits the equation.*

> How does the entry (10, 55) from the table show up on the graph? How is it related to the equation?

This pair of values represents how far Henri is from the starting line (55 meters—the 45-meter head start plus the 10 meters he has walked) at 10 seconds. It is a point on the graph for Henri. The values can be substituted for the time and distance variables in Henri's equation to show that they fit that as well.

Parts B and C relate to the point at which Emile overtakes Henri as it shows up in the table and the graph.

Talk about the follow-up to reinforce students' understanding of these ideas. Questions 1 and 2 are a preliminary introduction to solving equations but, at this stage, students can answer them using a table or a graph or reasoning about the situation. Question 3 asks which of the lines is steeper, foreshadowing the concept of the slope of a line. Question 5 informally introduces the concept of the *y*-intercept by asking questions about the point where the lines cross the *y*-axis.

Additional Answers

Answers to Problem 2.2

A. As the walking rate increases, the constant difference between consecutive values for the distance increases. Terry walks at 1 mph, so the difference is 1; Jade walks at 2 mph, so the difference is 2.

Time (seconds)	Terry	Jade	Jerome
0	0	0	0
1	1	2	2.5
2	2	4	5
3	3	6	7.5
4	4	8	10
5	5	10	12.5
6	6	12	15
7	7	14	17.5
8	8	16	20
9	9	18	22.5
10	10	20	25

Distance (meters)

B. As the walking rate increases, the steepness of the line increases. (Note: Students might notice that the vertical distance on the graph for Jade is double that for Terry.)

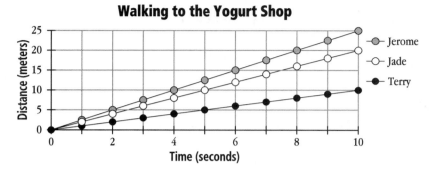

Walking to the Yogurt Shop

Answers to Problem 2.3

A. 1.

Distance	Money owed		
(miles)	Leanne	Gilberto	Alana
0	$0	$0	$5.00
1	1	2	5.50
2	2	4	6.00
3	3	6	6.50
4	4	8	7.00
5	5	10	7.50
6	6	12	8.00
7	7	14	8.50
8	8	16	9.00
9	9	18	9.50
10	10	20	10.00

2.

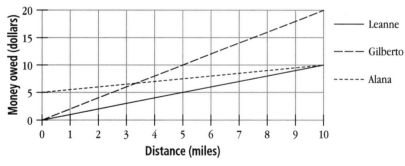

Walkathon Earnings

3. Leanne: $A = d$; Gilberto: $A = 2d$; Alana: $A = 0.50d + 5$, where A is the amount of money a sponsor owes and d is the distance walked in miles

B. As the amount pledged per mile increases, the change from entry to entry in the amount of money owed increases (the amount owed is greater with a greater rate per mile). In the graph, the steepness of the line increases. In the equation, d (the distance walked) is multiplied by a greater number.

C. Under Leanne's rule the sponsor would owe $8, under Gilberto's rule $16, and under Alana's rule $9. Students may have reasoned with the equations, read from the graph, or read from the table.

D. Under Leanne's plan, a student must walk 10 miles. Under Gilberto's plan, a sponsor would owe twice as much, so the student would need to walk only half as far, or

5 miles. Under Alana's plan, there is a $5 donation up front, so the distance walked must generate an additional $5. The student has to walk 2 miles for every $1, or 10 miles to raise the additional $5.

E. Alana's fixed donation of $5 is represented in the table as the amount of money a sponsor owes if a students does not walk at all (0 miles). In the graph, $5 is the point at which Alana's line crosses the "Money owed" axis. In the equation, $y = 0.5d + 5$, it is represented with the addition of the constant term 5.

Answers to Problem 2.3 Follow-Up

2. a. Possible answer: $A = 3d$ (Note: The equation should have a coefficient greater than 2 to be steeper than any of the other three lines.)

    b. Possible answer: $A = 10 + 0.4d$ (Note: The equation should have a coefficient less than 0.5.)

Walkathon Earnings

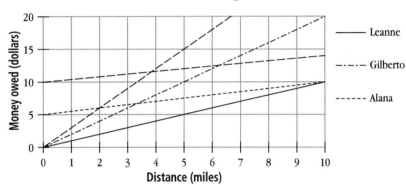

Answers to Problem 2.5

A. 1.

Time (seconds)	Henri's distance from starting line (meters)	Emile's distance from starting line (meters)
0	45	0
10	55	25
20	65	50
30	75	75
40	85	100

2.

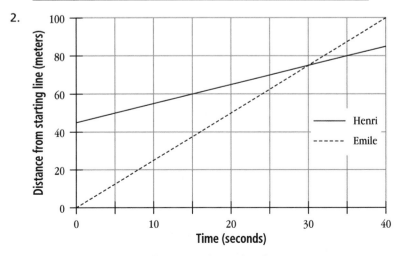

3. Henri: $d = t + 45$ (or $d = 1t + 45$); Emile: $d = 2.5t$

B. Emile overtakes Henri after 75 m. This is the point in the table where the time and distance for the brothers are equal and the point on the graph where the lines cross.

C. Emile overtakes Henri after 30 s. This is the point in the table where the time and distance for the brothers are equal and the point on the graph where the lines cross.

Answers to Problem 2.5 Follow-Up

6. a.

Time (seconds)	Distance (meters)
0	20
1	22
2	24
3	26
4	28
5	30
6	32
7	34

ACE Answers

Applications

7. Similarities: In tables a and b, the x value changes at a constant rate of 1; this isn't true in table c. Differences: In table a, y doesn't change at all; in tables b and c it does. In table c, y changes at a constant rate; this isn't true in table b. (Note: The patterns in tables a and c are similar in that there is an apparent constant change between successive y values—0, 0, 0, . . . in table a and $^-4$, $^-4$, $^-4$, . . . in table c. The difference is that table c does not show consecutive values of x, which means that the change in y values is not really constant, making the graph of table c nonlinear. The graph of table b is definitely nonlinear; it graphs a parabola; it is in fact quadratic. Its table indicates this nonlinearity by the nonconstant rate of change between successive y values.)

12e. Ingrid's line is steeper. On the graph, her line is more vertical. The faster the person travels, the steeper the line. (Note: Later, when students are able to write equations to represent graphs like this, they will see that the steepest line has the greatest coefficient for the variable on the x-axis. It may be interesting to note that the lines continue after Ingrid and Tara meet. Students may want to discuss what this part of the graph means.)

Connections

18a. Possible answer: The graph crosses the y-axis below the x-axis.

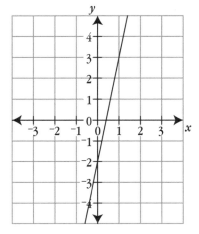

x	y
$^-1$	$^-7$
0	$^-2$
1	3
2	8

18b. Possible answer: The line falls as the values of *x* increase. It is like coming down stairs rather than going up stairs.

x	y
−1	5
0	3
1	1
2	−1

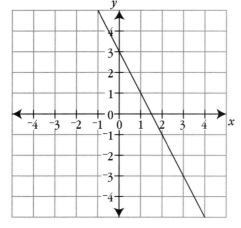

18c. $y = 2x - 1$; Possible observation: The graph crosses the *y*-axis below the *x*-axis.

x	y
−2	−5
0	−1
$\frac{1}{2}$	0
3	5

Extensions

21a.

Distance (miles)	NYC to SF time (hours)	SF to NYC time (hours)
0	0.00	0.00
200	0.74	0.61
400	1.48	1.21
600	2.22	1.82
800	2.96	2.42
1000	3.70	3.03
1200	4.44	3.64
1400	5.19	4.24
1600	5.93	4.85
1800	6.67	5.45
2000	7.41	6.06
2200	8.15	6.67
2400	8.89	7.27
2600	9.63	7.88
2800	10.37	8.48
3000	11.11	9.09

22b. The populations of Deep Valley, Nowhere, and Swampville are somewhat close and may easily be represented on the same graph. Putting Mount Silicon on the same vertical scale is difficult because its population increased so rapidly. Ranges will vary; students should support their choices. The horizontal scales are the same on the graphs shown below.

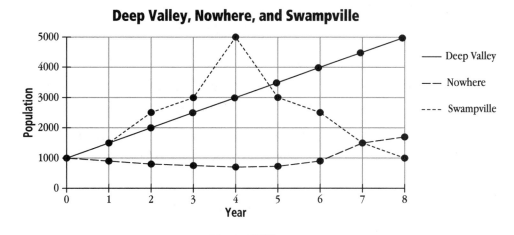

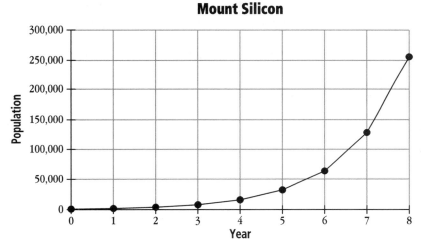

Mathematical Reflections

2. The rate—the meters per unit of time or the dollars per unit of distance—appears in the equation as the number multiplied by the independent variable (time or distance in this case); for example, if a person walks 7 mph, we can write $d = 7t$; if a walkathon participant charges $5 per mile, we can write $A = 5d$. In the graph, the rate affects the steepness of the line. In the table, the rate is the difference in the dependent variable (distance traveled or amount owed) per unit change in the independent variable; for example, as the participant walks from 1 mile to 2 miles, the amount the sponsor will owe increases $5. (Note: A walking rate and a payment rate are both ratios. Students may not see this connection and may need a class discussion to make these points.)

4. Graphs give a "pictorial history" of the relationship. They can be used to answer questions if the answers don't have to be exact. Equations give exact answers, but the equation for a relationship is not always known. Tables may or may not be easy to extend to find answers.

Exploring Lines with a Graphing Calculator

In Problem 3.1, Getting to the Point, students connect tables, graphs, and equations and interpret points on a graph in the context of the walkathon. In Problem 3.2, Graphing Lines, students use the graphing calculator to make graphical representations of relationships, and they focus on observing what happens in each form of representation—graph, table, and equation—to the dependent variable as the independent variable changes. In Problem 3.3, Finding Solutions, the equations are revisited, with an emphasis on solving equations and observing the relationship between the general rule for all values of the independent and dependent variables and the equation for specific values of the variables by reading data pairs from graphs and tables on the graphing calculator. In Problem 3.4, Planning a Skating Party, students apply what they have learned to try to find a common solution to two different equations. They find their answer graphically, and they interpret it in the context of the problem. Students are then introduced to the $y = mx + b$ form of a linear equation and explore the significance of m and b on the other two representations.

Mathematical and Problem-Solving Goals

- **To connect solutions in graphs and tables to solutions of equations**

- **To find a solution common to two linear equations by graphing**

- **To understand how the y-intercept appears in tables and equations**

- **To understand how the rate of change (the coefficient m) appears in equations and affects the graph of a line**

Materials		
Problem	**For students**	**For the teacher**
All	Graphing calculators	Transparencies 3.1 to 3.4 (optional), overhead display model of students' graphing calculator (optional)
3.1		Transparencies of the graph, table, and equations from Problem 2.3 (optional)

Student Pages 35–52   Teaching the Investigation 52a–52q

Exploring Lines with a Graphing Calculator

In the last investigation, you read about the walkathon that Ms. Chang's class is participating in. You considered three possible pledge plans. If *A* represents the dollars owed and *d* represents the number of miles walked, we can express these plans with the equations below.

- Leanne's plan: $A = d$
- Gilberto's plan: $A = 2d$
- Alana's plan: $A = 5 + 0.5d$

In this investigation, you will learn how to use a graphing calculator to help you answer questions like these:

What does Leanne's equation mean?

Using Gilberto's plan, how much will a sponsor owe a student who walks 5 miles?

Using Alana's plan, how far will a student have to walk to earn $17 from each sponsor?

Did you know?

Have you ever seen a walking race? You may have thought the walking style of the racers seemed rather strange. Race walkers must follow two rules:

1. The walker must always have one foot in contact with the ground.
2. The walker's leg must be straight from the time it strikes the ground until it passes under the body.

A champion race walker can cover a mile in about 6.5 minutes. It takes most people 15 to 20 minutes to walk a mile.

Getting to the Point

At a Glance

Grouping: individuals, then pairs

Launch

- Talk about the equations for the three pledge plans.

- Review the tables, graphs, and equations from Problem 2.3.

- Informally discuss how a point on a graph relates to a solution of an equation.

- Have students work on the problem individually, then share answers in pairs.

Explore

- If students have found only one question, ask if they can find another.

Summarize

- Have students share their answers and strategies.

- Have pairs do the follow-up, and review the answers.

- Assist the class with using window settings with the trace feature.

Assignment Choices

ACE questions 24–26 and unassigned choices from earlier problems

---

3.1 Getting to the Point

To work on this problem, you will need the tables and graphs you made in Problem 2.3.

> ### Problem 3.1
>
> Look at the table and the graph you made for Alana's pledge plan.
>
> **A.** The point (14, 12) is on the graph of Alana's plan. Write a question you could answer by locating this point.
>
> **B.** How can you use the equation for Alana's plan to check the answer to the question you wrote in part A?
>
> **C. 1.** For a sponsor to owe a student $17 under Alana's pledge plan, how many miles would the student have to walk?
>
> **2.** Was the graph or the equation more helpful in answering part 1?

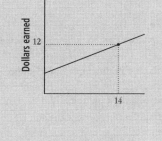

▦ Problem 3.1 Follow-Up

1. Aretha is trying to answer a question about Alana's pledge plan. She writes $A = 5 + 0.5(28)$. What question is she trying to answer?

2. **a.** Daniel is trying to answer a question about Alana's pledge plan. He writes $46 = 5 + 0.5d$. What question is he trying to answer?

   b. Daniel decides to use a calculator to help him answer the question from part a. He enters Alana's equation as $Y_1 = 5 + 0.5X$ and presses $\boxed{\text{GRAPH}}$. He uses the $\boxed{\text{TRACE}}$ key to search for an answer. Help Daniel interpret the information in the window below to determine an answer to his question.

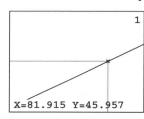

   c. Daniel could have answered the question by making a table. Use your calculator to make a table for $Y_1 = 5 + 0.5X$. Copy a section of the table you could use to answer Daniel's question.

36 Moving Straight Ahead

Answers to Problem 3.1

A. The point (14, 12) represents answers to these questions: If a participant walks 14 mi, how much money will each sponsor owe? If a participant collects $12, how many miles did he or she walk?

B. $12 = 5 + 0.5(14)$

C. 1. 24 miles

   2. Some students may read this point from the graph; some may reason from the equation.

Answers to Problem 3.1 Follow-Up

1. Aretha is trying to answer the question, What would a sponsor owe if a participant walks 28 miles?

36 Investigation 3

3.2 Graphing Lines

A graphing calculator can be helpful for answering questions like those in Problem 3.1 and Problem 3.1 Follow-Up. When you use a graphing calculator, you need to make decisions about the range of values and the scale interval for each axis. These values are called *window settings* because they determine what part of the graph will be displayed in the calculator's window.

Below are two examples of window settings and the corresponding graph windows. For each example, try to make sense of what the ranges and the scale intervals are for the *x*- and *y*-axes.

Window 1

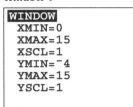
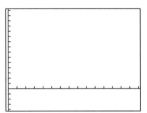

Window 2

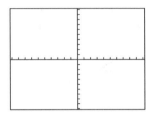

The settings for window 1 use a different range for each axis. The range of *x* values is from 0 to 15, which is a spread of 15 units. The range of *y* values is from ⁻4 to 15, which is a spread of 19 units. The scale interval for both axes is 1, which means that each tick mark represents 1 unit.

Window 2 is the *standard window* on many graphing calculators. These are the settings the calculator uses unless you change them. In this window, both axes have a range from ⁻10 to 10 and a scale interval of 1.

Notice that, in each window, the length of 1 unit (the distance between tick marks) is different on the *x*-axis than it is on the *y*-axis. Can you explain why?

Investigation 3: Exploring Lines with a Graphing Calculator **37**

Graphing Lines

- - - - - - - - - - - - -
At a Glance

Grouping: individuals, then pairs

Launch

- As a class, experiment with window settings and using the trace feature.

- Discuss the "Think about this!" example.

Explore

- As a class, use the graphing calculator to examine equation i. *(optional)*

- Group students having difficulty using the calculator with students who can use it easily.

Summarize

- Discuss students' answers to the problem.

- Ask students to substitute coordinates from the tables into the equations to check that they get an equality.

- Go over the follow-up.

---

2. a. Daniel is trying to answer the question, What distance would have to be walked to collect $46?

    b. The *y* value at this point is almost 46, and the *x* value is almost 82, so this means about 82 miles would have to be walked to collect $46.

    c. Possible table:

x	y
79	44.5
80	45
81	45.5
82	46

Assignment Choices

ACE questions 1–4, 6, 27, and unassigned choices from earlier problems (1–4 require a graphing calculator)

Think about this!

How far would a student have to walk to raise $8.50 from each sponsor under Alana's plan?

Ali and Tamara are using graphing calculators to answer this question. They both enter the equation $Y_1 = 5 + 0.5X$. Ali uses window 1 for his graph, and Tamara uses window 2. Both students use TRACE to find the solution.

Window 1 (Ali's Graph)

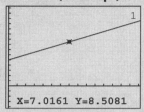

X=7.0161 Y=8.5081

Window 2 (Tamara's Graph)

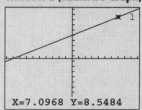

X=7.0968 Y=8.5484

- What does the X value displayed at the bottom of each window mean? What does the Y value mean?

- How could you interpret the information displayed in the windows to answer the question above? How could you check your answer?

You have explored pledge plans suggested by Leanne, Gilberto, and Alana. In this problem, you will explore some plans suggested by other students.

Finding Solutions

Problem 3.2

In A–D, consider the following suggested pledge plans. In each equation, y is the amount owed in dollars, and x is the number of miles walked.

i. $y = 3x$ **ii.** $y = {}^-2x$ **iii.** $y = 5x - 3$
iv. $y = {}^-x + 6$ **v.** $y = 2$

A. What does each pledge plan mean?

B. Without using your graphing calculator, make a table of x and y values for each pledge plan. Use the x values 1, 2, 3, 4, and 5. Use your tables to help you decide which plans are reasonable. Explain how you made your decisions.

C. Graph each pledge plan with a graphing calculator. Use a window that shows the graph clearly. Make a sketch of the graph you see.

D. For each pledge plan, tell whether the y values increase, decrease, or stay the same as the x values increase. How can you tell from the graph? From the table? From the equation?

■ **Problem 3.2 Follow-Up**

1. For each of the five pledge plans, give the coordinates of the points where the line crosses the x- and y-axes. (Check that the coordinates you give fit the equation. Sometimes the decimal values your calculator gives are only approximations.)

2. Ali says that $x = {}^-1$ makes the equation ${}^-8 = {}^-3 + 5x$ true. Tamara tries this value in the equation. She says Ali is wrong because ${}^-3 + 5({}^-1)$ is ${}^-2$, not ${}^-8$. Why do you think these students found different answers?

3.3 Finding Solutions

In this problem, you will explore the relationship between a general equation, such as $y = 5 + 0.5x$, and the equation you get by substituting a value for either x or y, such as $8 = 5 + 0.5x$ or $y = 5 + 0.5(3)$. You will continue to work with the pledge plan equations from Problem 3.2.

By now you've probably noticed that values for x and y come in pairs. In the pledge equations, if you know the distance walked, x, you can find the amount a sponsor owes, y. If you know the amount a sponsor owes, y, you can find the distance walked, x. You can express related x and y values as **coordinate pairs** in the form (x, y). For example, the pairs (6, 8) and (3, 6.5) fit Alana's equation. Can you explain what each pair means?

Launch

■ Go over the example of the general equation and the two related equations in the introduction.

Explore

■ Circulate as groups work, helping them to understand the questions as necessary.

■ Remind students of the tables and graphs they made for the equations in Problem 3.2.

Summarize

■ Have groups share solutions and strategies.

■ Make sure students understand the relationship between a general equation and specific instances of the equation.

■ Let students work on the follow-up individually, then review the questions as a class.

Answers to Problem 3.2

See page 52k.

Answers to Problem 3.2 Follow-Up

1.   i. x- and y-axes: (0, 0)

     ii. x- and y-axes: (0, 0)

     iii. x-axis: (0, ${}^-3$), y-axis: ($\frac{3}{5}$, 0)

     iv. x-axis: (0, 6), y-axis: (6, 0)

     v. y-axis: (0, 2)

2.   See page 52n.

Assignment Choices

ACE questions 18–21, 28, 29, and unassigned choices from earlier problems

Problem 3.3

In A–D, consider the following equations.

i. $y = 3x$ **ii.** $y = {}^-2x$ **iii.** $y = 5x - 3$
iv. $y = {}^-x + 6$ **v.** $y = 2$

A. 1. Which equation has a graph you can trace to find the value of x that makes $^-8 = 5x - 3$ a true statement?

2. Use your graphing calculator to find the value of x. We call this value the *solution* to the equation $^-8 = 5x - 3$.

B. 1. Which equation has a table you can use to find the value of x that makes $6.8 = {}^-2x$ a true statement?

2. Make a table with your graphing calculator, and find the value of x. Copy the part of the table you used to find the solution.

C. Find solutions for the equations $^-8 = 5x - 3$ and $6.8 = {}^-2x$ by reasoning about what the equations mean rather than by using graphs or tables. Explain how you found the solutions.

D. 1. How does finding the solution to $^-8 = 5x - 3$ help you find a coordinate pair that fits the equation $y = 5x - 3$?

2. Find three other coordinate pairs that fit the equation $y = 5x - 3$. How can you prove your coordinate pairs fit the equation?

■ **Problem 3.3 Follow-Up**

1. Are the points for the coordinate pairs you found for $y = 5x - 3$ on the graph of $y = 5x - 3$? Explain your answer.

2. In part B of Problem 3.3, you found the solution to the equation $6.8 = {}^-2x$. Based on the solution, what coordinate pair do you know must fit the equation $y = {}^-2x$? How is this coordinate pair related to the graph of $y = {}^-2x$?

3. a. By substituting values for y, write three equations that are related to the equation $y = {}^-3x + 6$.

b. Solve each of your equations from part a. Explain how you found each solution.

c. Use the solutions from part b to find the coordinates of three points on the graph of $y = {}^-3x + 6$.

d. Use your graphing calculator to check your answers to part c. Explain how you know your answers are correct.

Answers to Problem 3.3

See page 52n.

Answers to Problem 3.3 Follow-Up

1. All the coordinate pairs found, such as ($^-1$, $^-8$), are on the graph of $y = 5x - 3$. The equation is a description of all the ordered pairs that lie on that line, so any pair of values that fits the equation will be on the graph.

2. The ordered pair is ($^-3.4$, 6.8). This means that the graph of the equation $y = {}^-2x$ goes through the point ($^-3.4$, 6.8).

3. See page 52n.

Planning a Skating Party

You have studied lots of linear equations. Here are some examples:

$$y = x \qquad y = 2x \qquad y = 5 + 0.5x \qquad y = 45 + x \qquad y = {}^-3x + 6$$

All the linear equations you have studied can be written in the form $y = mx + b$. For the equation $y = x$, m is 1 and b is 0. For $y = 2x$, m is 2 and b is 0. For $y = 5 + 0.5x$, m is 0.5 and b is 5. What are the values of m and b for $y = 45 + x$ and $y = {}^-3x + 6$?

When we substitute 0 for x in $y = mx + b$, we get $y = b$. This means that the point $(0, b)$ lies on the line. The point $(0, b)$ is called the **y-intercept.** It is the point where the line crosses the y-axis. To save time, we sometimes refer to the number b, rather than the point $(0, b)$, as the y-intercept. You found y-intercepts for some equations in Problem 3.2 Follow-Up.

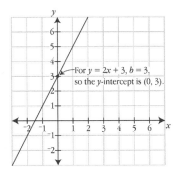

For $y = 2x + 3$, $b = 3$, so the y-intercept is $(0, 3)$.

If the b in $y = mx + b$ is 0 (in other words, if the equation is of the form $y = mx$) then the y-intercept is $(0, 0)$, or the **origin.** For example, the graphs of Leanne's pledge plan $y = x$ and Gilberto's pledge plan $y = 2x$ both pass through the origin.

The m in $y = mx + b$ is called the **coefficient** of x. In Investigation 2, you found that the value of m indicates the steepness of the line. For example, when you graphed equations for students' walking rates, you found that the graph of $y = 2x$ was steeper than the graph of $y = x$ but less steep than the graph of $y = 2.5x$. You also discovered that the sign of m—that is, whether m is positive or negative—determines whether a line slants upward or downward.

In the last problem, you used a graphing calculator to find specific points on the graphs of linear equations. In this problem, you will use a graphing calculator to find the point where two graphs cross. This point is called the **point of intersection** of the graphs.

At a Glance

Grouping: pairs

Launch

- Spend time demonstrating the use of graphing calculators to analyze the two equations from Problem 2.5.

- Talk about finding and interpreting points of intersection and adjusting window settings.

- Discuss the new terminology presented in the student edition.

Explore

- As pairs work on the problem, have those who are struggling work with others who understand how to use the calculator and the trace feature.

Summarize

- Have students share their answers and discuss their strategies.

- Go through the follow-up questions as a class.

Assignment Choices

part 1: ACE questions 5–8, 22, 23; *part 2:* ACE questions 9–17; and unassigned choices from earlier problems (7–12, 15, and 16 require a graphing calculator)

Assessment

It is appropriate to use Quiz A after this problem.

Problem 3.4

Suppose your class is planning a skating party to celebrate the end of the school year. Your committee is in charge of finding a place to rent in-line skates for a reasonable price. You get quotes from two companies:

> Roll-Away Skates charges $5 per person.
> Wheelie's Skates and Stuff charges $100 plus $3 per person.

Which company should you choose if you want to keep the cost to a minimum? Explain how you made your choice.

▨ Problem 3.4 Follow-Up

In these problems, let y be the total cost to rent the skates and x be the number of people attending the party.

1. a. For each company, write an equation for the relationship between the number of people and the cost.

b. In the same window, graph the equations for both companies.

c. What range of values did you use for the number of people? For the rental cost? How did you select these ranges?

2. a. On which graph is the point (8, 40)? What does this point mean in terms of the cost to rent skates?

b. On which graph is the point (8, 124)? What does this point mean in terms of the cost to rent skates?

c. Find the point of intersection of the two graphs. What does this point mean in terms of the cost to rent skates?

Answer to Problem 3.4

Possible answer: From the table (and to a lesser extent from the graph), it is clear that when the number of students is 50, the two costs are identical. For more than 50 students, Wheelie's Skates and Stuff charges less than Roll-Away Skates. For fewer than 50 students, Roll-Away Skates offers the better deal.

X	Y₁	Y₂
44	220	232
45	225	235
46	230	238
47	235	241
48	240	244
49	245	247
50	250	250
X=50		

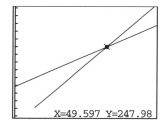

X=49.597 Y=247.98

3. If you write a linear equation in the form $y = mx + b$, the y-intercept is $(0, b)$.

    a. Find the y-intercepts for the equations you graphed in question 1.

    b. What do the y-intercepts mean in terms of the cost to rent skates?

    c. How do the y-intercepts appear on the graphs?

    d. Display the table for the equations. How do the y-intercepts appear in the table?

4. What are the coefficients of x in the equations you graphed in question 1? What do these coefficients mean in terms of the cost to rent skates? What effect do the coefficients have on the graphs?

5. Which company would you choose if 100 students are planning to attend the party? Why?

6. If your budget for skate rental is $250, how many pairs of skates can you rent from each company?

Answers to Problem 3.4 Follow-Up

See page 52o.

Answers

Applications

1a. See page 52p.

1b. Possible answer: *x* and *y* values from 10 to ⁻10

1c. increase

1d. (0, 0)

1e. Possible answer: (⁻4, ⁻6), (1, 1.5), (5, 7.5)

2a. See page 52p.

2b. Possible answer: *x* and *y* values from 10 to ⁻10

2c. decrease

2d. (0, 10)

2e. Possible answer: (⁻2, 16), (0, 10), (3.5, ⁻0.5)

3a. See page 52p.

3b. Possible answer: *x* and *y* values from 10 to ⁻10

3c. decrease

3d. (0, 6)

3e. Possible answer: (⁻1, 8), (3, 0), (8, ⁻10)

4a. See page 52p.

4b. Possible answer: *x* and *y* values from 10 to ⁻10

4c. increase

4d. (0, 5)

4e. Possible answer: (⁻3, ⁻1), (0, 5), (2.5, 10)

5a. 75 candy bars

5b. For 50 candy bars, the revenue would be $33; for 125 candy bars, it would be $83. (Note: Students are reading answers from the graph, so some inaccuracy is expected.)

5c. For a revenue of $200, the band would have to sell 300 candy bars. The cost would be $125, leaving a profit of $75.

As you work on these ACE questions, use your calculator whenever you need it.

Applications

In 1–4, do parts a–e.

1. $y = 1.5x$ **2.** $y = {}^-3x + 10$ **3.** $y = {}^-2x + 6$ **4.** $y = 2x + 5$

    a. Graph the equation on your calculator, and make a sketch of the line you see.

    b. Give the ranges of values you used for the *x*- and *y*-axes.

    c. Do the *y* values increase, decrease, or stay the same as the *x* values increase?

    d. Give the *y*-intercept.

    e. List the coordinates of three points on the line.

5. The school band decides to sell chocolate bars to raise money for an upcoming trip. The cost and the revenue (total sales, or income) of selling the candy bars are represented on the graph below.

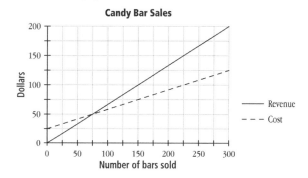

Candy Bar Sales

    a. How many candy bars must the band sell to break even?

    b. What would be the revenue from selling 50 candy bars? 125 candy bars?

    c. How many candy bars must the band sell for the revenue to be $200? How much of this revenue would be profit?

6. a. At the left below, the graphs from question 5 are shown in a calculator's graph window. The window settings are shown at the right. Copy the graph window, and use the window settings to label the axes to show where the scale values 50, 100, 150, and so on are located.

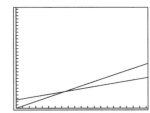

```
WINDOW
  XMIN=0
  XMAX=200
  XSCL=10
  YMIN=0
  YMAX=300
  YSCL=10
```

b. Below are the same two graphs shown in a different graph window. Copy the graph window, and use the window settings to label the tick marks.

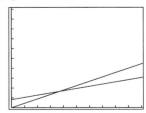

```
WINDOW
  XMIN=0
  XMAX=200
  XSCL=20
  YMIN=0
  YMAX=300
  YSCL=30
```

7. In a–c, use the equation $y = 2x + 10$.

   a. By making a graph on your calculator, find the value of y when $x = 15$.

   b. By making a graph on your calculator, find the value of x when $y = 35$.

   c. Make a sketch of the graph of $y = 2x + 10$, and label the points that represent the pairs of values you found in parts a and b.

8. In a–c, use the equation $y = -3.5x - 9$.

   a. By making a graph on your calculator, find the value of y when $x = 5$.

   b. By making a graph on your calculator, find the value of x when $y = -40$.

   c. Make a sketch of the graph of $y = -3.5x - 9$, and label the points that represent the pairs of values you found in parts a and b.

Investigation 3: Exploring Lines with a Graphing Calculator 45

6a.

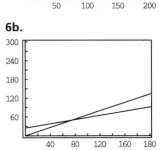

6b.

7a. when $x = 15$, $y = 40$ (Note: Students' accuracy will depend on their window settings. They will not likely get exact values using the trace feature. This is acceptable.)

7b. when $y = 35$, $x = 12.5$

7c. See below left.

8a. when $x = 5$, $y = -26.5$

8b. when $y = -40$, $x =$ about 8.85

8c. See below left.

7c.

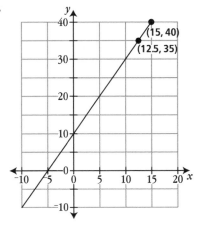

8c.

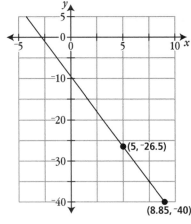

9a. See page 52q.

(Note: In 9–12, accuracy will depend on the ranges students use. They will not likely get exact values using the trace key. This is acceptable.)

9a. See page 52q.

9b. (⁻4, 4)

9c. The values may not fit exactly, but they should be close. (Note: Students may suggest that their values are not accurate because of the calculators. You might suggest that students could improve this accuracy by using better windows or other techniques that are available on their calculators.)

10a. See page 52q.

10b. (7.1, ⁻2.9)

10c. The values may not fit exactly, but they should be close.

11a. See page 52q.

11b. (⁻0.67, 9.33)

11c. The values may not fit exactly, but they should be close.

12a. See page 52q.

12b. (1, 6)

12c. The values may not fit exactly, but they should be close.

13a. The new equation is $d = t$ or $y = x$; it is a line passing through the point (0, 0).

13b. The new line has the same slope as before but a lower y-intercept, and the equation does not have 45 added to it.

13c. Henri's head start was the y-intercept at 45 and the 45 was added to the equation.

In 9–12, do parts a–c.

9. $y = 5x + 24$ and $y = ⁻3x – 8$

10. $y = ⁻2.5x + 15$ and $y = x – 10$

11. $y = x + 10$ and $y = 8 – 2x$

12. $y = 6$ and $y = 4 + 2x$

   a. With your graphing calculator, graph both equations in the same window. Use window settings that allow you to see the point where the two graphs intersect. What ranges of x and y values did you use for your window?

   b. Find the point of intersection for the graphs.

   c. Test the point of intersection you found by substituting its coordinates into the equations. Do the coordinates fit the equations exactly? Explain why or why not.

13. In Problem 2.4, Emile gave Henri a head start of 45 meters. Now suppose Emile does not give his brother a head start.

   a. Write a new equation for the distance Henri is from the starting line after a given number of seconds. Describe the graph of this new equation.

   b. How do this new graph and equation compare with the original graph and equation?

   c. What effect did Henri's head start have on the original graph? On the original equation?

14. For Valentine's Day, students at Holmes Middle School will sell roses to raise money for a school party. The students can buy the roses from a wholesaler for 50¢ each. In addition to buying the roses, they need to spend $60 for ribbon and paper to wrap the flowers and for materials to advertise the sale. They will sell each flower for $1.30. They will take orders in advance so that they know how many roses they will need.

   a. How many roses must the students sell to break even?

   b. How much profit will the students earn if they sell 50 roses? 100 roses? 200 roses?

14a. 75 roses (Note: Students can look at the intersection of the cost equation, $y = 0.5x + 60$, and the revenue equation, $y = 1.3x$.)

14b. If the students sell 50 roses, they lose 65 – 85 = $20; if they sell 100 roses, they make a profit of 130 – 110 = $20; and if they sell 200 roses, they make a profit of 260 – 160 = $100.

15. A new movie theater opened in Lani's neighborhood. The theater offers a yearly membership for which customers pay a fee of $50, after which they pay only $1 per movie. Nonmembers pay $4.50 per movie. Lani is trying to figure out whether to buy a membership. She writes these cost equations.

$$C_M = 50 + n \qquad \text{and} \qquad C_N = 4.5n$$

where n is the number of movies seen in one year, C_M is the yearly cost in dollars for a member, and C_N is the yearly cost in dollars for a nonmember.

a. If Lani sees ten movies this year, what would be her cost under each plan?

b. How many movies must Lani see this year to make the yearly membership a better deal?

c. What does the y-intercept in each equation tell you about this situation?

d. What does the coefficient of n in each equation tell you about this situation?

In 16 and 17, use the following information: You are on the committee to select a DJ for a school party. The committee has obtained price quotes from three DJs:

Tom's Tunes charges $60 an hour.
Solidus' Sounds charges $100 plus $40 an hour.
Light Plastic charges $175 plus $30 an hour.

16. **a.** Which DJ would you choose? What variables might affect your decision?

b. For each DJ, write an equation you could use to calculate the total cost from the number of hours worked. Let y be the total cost and x be the number of hours worked.

c. Graph all three equations in the same window of your calculator. Make a sketch of the graphs you see.

d. What information does the coefficient of x represent in each equation?

e. What information does the y-intercept represent in each equation?

15a. member: 50 + 10 = $60, nonmember: 4.5(10) = $45

15b. The point $n = 14.3$ is the break-even point, but it does not make sense to see 0.3 of a movie (you would still have to pay for the full movie). If you see 15 movies, the member price is a better deal.

15c. The y-intercept tells the amount paid for the membership ($50 versus $0).

15d. The coefficient of n tells the cost of each movie ($1 versus $4.50).

16a. Answers will vary. One possible variable is the length of time the DJ will work.

16b. Tom's Tunes: $y = 60x$, Solidus' Sounds: $y = 40x + 100$, Light Plastic: $y = 30x + 175$

16c. See page 52q.

16d. The coefficient of x gives the cost per hour, or the DJ's hourly rate.

16e. The y-intercept gives the initial charge for each DJ.

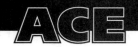

17a. 5 hours, $300

17b. Tom's Tunes: $510, Solidus' Sounds: $440, Light Plastic: $430 (Note: The table feature might be particularly useful for this problem. Students could scroll down to the line with $x = 8.5$. They may need help setting their tables to show smaller increments.)

17c. Tom's Tunes: 7.5 h, Solidus' Sounds: 8.75 h, Light Plastic: about 9.2 h (Note: Students could solve this by tracing the graphs or using the tables created by their calculators.)

Connections

18. values greater than $^-2.5$ (Note: Students are likely to give integer answers for problems 18, 20, and 21, such as greater than $^-2$.)

19. All values of x will make y negative.

20. values less than 2.5

21. values less than $\frac{1}{6}$

22a. Locate the y value of 22. The corresponding x value is 26.

22b. Trace to the point where the y value is 22. The corresponding x value will be 26.

17. Use your calculator to answer a–c.

a. For what number of hours are the costs for Tom's Tunes and Solidus' Sounds equal? What is the cost for that time?

b. What would be the cost for each DJ if he or she worked $8\frac{1}{2}$ hours?

c. You have $450 to spend on a DJ. How many hours could each DJ work for this price?

Connections

In 18–21, tell what values of x make y negative.

18. $y = {}^-2x - 5$ **19.** $y = {}^-5$ **20.** $y = 2x - 5$ **21.** $y = \frac{3}{2}x - \frac{1}{4}$

22. In a–c, explain how you could use the display shown to find the solution to $22 = 100 - 3x$.

a.

X	Y1
21	37
22	34
23	31
24	28
25	25
26	22

Y1=100-3X

b.

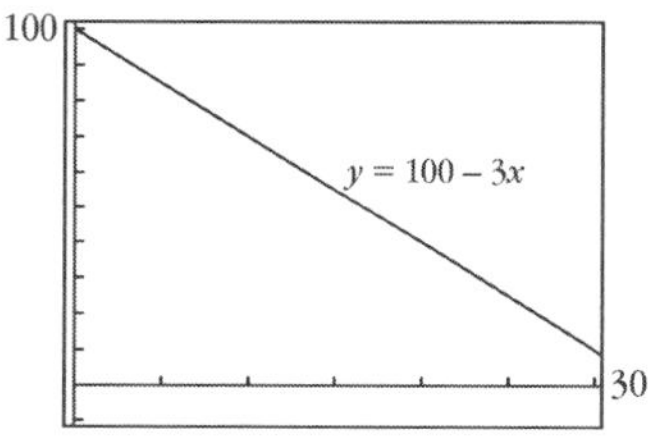

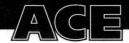

c.

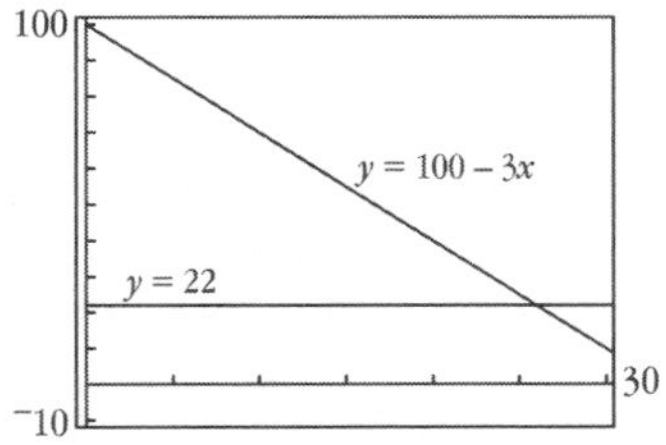

23. In a and b, explain how you could use the display shown to find the solution to $100 - 3x = 2x - 50$.

a.

X	Y1	Y2
25	25	0
26	22	2
27	19	4
28	16	6
29	13	8
30	10	10

Y2=2X-50

b.

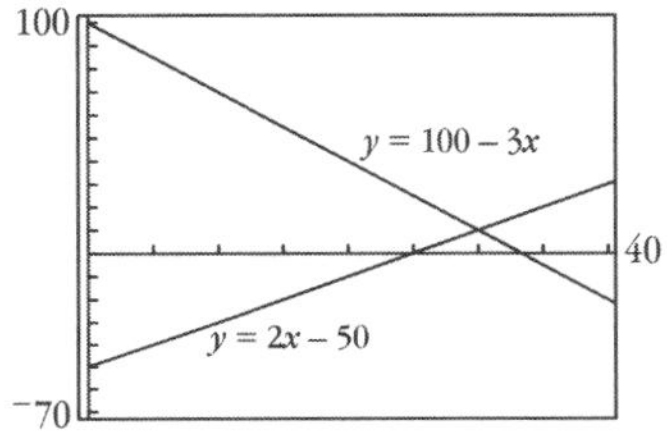

In 24–26, tell whether or not the equation represents a linear relationship, and explain your answer.

24. $y = 2x$ **25.** $y = \frac{2}{x}$ **26.** $y = x^2$

22c. The point of intersection gives the point where $y = 22$. At this point, $x = 26$.

23a. For each value of x, compare the values of y_1 and y_2 to find when they are equal. This happens at $y = 10$. The corresponding value for x is 30.

23b. Trace to the point of intersection, and read the value of x.

24. linear (Note: Students may look at the graphs or a table to explain their answers in 24–26. Looking at the graphs is the easiest way to determine linearity. To determine linearity from a table, students would have to look for a constant change in the y values.)

25. nonlinear

26. nonlinear

Extensions

27a. Each pair of lines is parallel. We know that m affects the steepness of the graph. Two equations with the same value for m will produce lines with the same steepness—that is, they will be parallel. The value of b shows where the line intercepts the y-axis.

27b. Each pair of lines is perpendicular. The values of m are opposite reciprocals.

27c. The lines may not look perpendicular on the graphing calculators. The screen is not a square, so that when the same scales are used for the x- and y-axes, the scales do not appear the same on the screen, thus distorting the relationship between the lines. (Note: The fact that the graphs do not appear to be perpendicular may be interesting to discuss. On some calculators, you can use a zoom feature to adjust for this distortion.)

27d. Sets iii and iv will produce parallel lines; sets i and ii will produce perpendicular lines.

Extensions

27. a. On grid paper, graph each pair of lines below on the same set of axes. Use the same scale for the x- and y-axes for each pair. When you are finished, look at the graphs for all four pairs of equations. What patterns do you observe? Use what you know about the influence of m and b on the graph of $y = mx + b$ to explain why these patterns might occur.

 i. $y = 1.2x + 3$ and $y = 1.2x$ **ii.** $y = 4$ and $y = {}^-2$

 iii. $y = x - 19$ and $y = 4 + x$ **iv.** $y = {}^-3.6x$ and $y = 5 - 3.6x$

b. On grid paper, graph each pair of lines below on the same set of axes. Use the same scale for the x- and y-axes. When you are finished, look at the graphs for all four pairs of equations. What patterns do you observe? Compare the coefficients of x in each pair, and describe any relationships you see.

 i. $y = 2x + 1$ and $y = -\frac{1}{2}x - 2$ **ii.** $y = x - 3$ and $y = {}^-x$

 iii. $y = x$ and $y = {}^-x$ **iv.** $y = \frac{5}{4}x$ and $y = -\frac{4}{5}x + 4$

c. Graph the equations from part b on your graphing calculator, using the same scales you used in your hand-drawn graphs. Explain any differences you see between the hand-drawn graphs and the calculator graphs.

d. Use your observations from parts a and b to predict the relationship between the graphs of the pairs of equations below. Check your predictions by graphing the equations.

 i. $y = 4x$ and $y = -\frac{1}{4}x$ **ii.** $y = x + 2$ and $y = {}^-x + 5$

 iii. $y = 0.5x + 2$ and $y = 0.5x - 2$ **iv.** $y = 2x + 1$ and $y = 2x$

28. For a given latitude and longitude, the temperature decreases as the altitude increases. The formula for calculating the temperature, T, at a given altitude is

$$T = t - \frac{d}{150}$$

where t is the ground temperature in degrees Celsius and d is the altitude in meters.

a. If the ground temperature is 0°C, what is the temperature at an altitude of 1500 meters?

b. If the temperature at an altitude of 300 meters is 26°C, what is the ground temperature?

29. a. Which one of the following points is on the line $y = 3x - 7$?

(3, 3) (3, 2) (3, 1) (3, 0)

Describe where each of the other three points is in relationship to the line.

b. Find another point on the line $y = 3x - 7$ and three more points above the line.

c. The equation $y = 3x - 7$ is true for (4, 5) and (7, 14). Find two points for which the inequality $y < 3x - 7$ is true and two points for which the inequality $y > 3x - 7$ is true.

28a. $T = 0 - \frac{1500}{150} =$ $0 - 10 = {}^-10°C$

28b. $26 = t - \frac{300}{150} = t - 2$; thus $t = 28°C$

29a. Point (3, 2) is on the line, (3, 3) is above the line, and the other two points are below the line.

29b. Possible answer: Point (1, ⁻4) is on the line, and points (1, ⁻3), (1, ⁻2), and (1, ⁻1) are above it.

29c. Possible answer: Since point (4, 5) satisfies $y = 3x - 7$, adjusting the y values to give (4, 4) or (4, 3) will give points that satisfy $y < 3x - 7$. Likewise, (4, 6) and (4, 7) satisfy $y > 3x - 7$.

Possible Answers

1. *Advantages:* The graphing calculator allows you to enter any equation, graph it, and find values of x to correspond to a given value of y, or vice versa. So if you have a relationship between two variables that can be written in the "$y =$" form, you can predict answers for one variable given the other. A table is easy to read, and on a calculator, easy to set to any accuracy.
Disadvantages: Setting the graph window takes reasoning and practice, and interpreting the output needs to be done with care.

2. In a table, the y-intercept is the data pair that has 0 for the first element, (0, ___).
On a graph, it is the place where the line crosses the y-axis. In an equation, it is the constant term b.

3. Some lines are steeper than others. Some slant up and some slant down. The m in the equation controls this. Greater values of m mean there is a greater rate of change in the situation, so the lines are steeper. Negative values of m give lines that slant down. The value of b gives the y-intercept.

4. We need to see whether $13 = 5 - 4(-2)$. The multiplication should be done first. Does $13 = 5 - (-8)$? Does $13 = 5 + 8$? The answer is yes. This means that the point (-2, 13) is on the line $y = 5 - 4x$.

Mathematical Reflections

In this investigation, you learned how to use tables and graphs to solve problems about linear relationships, and you discovered how a point in a table or on a graph relates to the corresponding equation. You also learned how to find the y-intercept of a relationship from a table, graph, or equation. These questions will help you summarize what you have learned:

① What are some of the advantages and disadvantages of using a graphing calculator to answer questions about linear situations?

② Explain how to find the y-intercept of a linear relationship from a table, from a graph, and from an equation.

③ In Investigation 2, you explored the effect that the rate has on the graph of a linear relationship. In this investigation, you looked at the meaning of particular points on the graph, including the y-intercept. Summarize what you know about the graph of a linear equation of the form $y = mx + b$.

④ To check whether a given point fits a linear relationship, you can make a table, trace a graph, or substitute the coordinates into an equation. When you substitute values into an equation, you need to be careful about the order in which you do the calculations. Check whether the point (-2, 13) is on the line $y = 5 - 4x$ by substituting the coordinates into the equation. Show and explain each step you take so that it is easy to see the order in which you did your calculations.

Think about your answers to these questions, discuss your ideas with other students and your teacher, and then write a summary of your findings in your journal.

Tips for the Linguistically Diverse Classroom

Original Rebus The Original Rebus technique is described in detail in *Getting to Know Connected Mathematics*. Students make a copy of the text before it is discussed. During the discussion, they generate their own rebuses for words they do not understand; the words are made comprehensible through pictures, objects, or demonstrations. Example: Question 1—Key words for which students might make rebuses are *advantages* (+), *disadvantages* (–), *graphing calculator* (rectangle showing a screen and keyboard), *linear situations* (two points on a grid connected by a straight line).

TEACHING THE INVESTIGATION

3.1 • Getting to the Point

In Problem 2.3, students made graphs and tables in their exploration of the walkathon; they informally made connections among points on a line, entries in a table, and solutions to an equation. In this investigation, students revisit these representations and use them to answer questions. They will find that a point on a graph represents a particular solution and that this solution can be checked in the equation. (The same solution can be found from an equation, but at this time students may only be able to check that the graphical solution fits the equation. They will manipulate symbols to solve an equation in a later investigation.)

Launch

Read through the introduction with your students, and discuss what each walkathon equation means. Display graphs, tables, and equations from Problem 2.3 on the board or overhead projector.

> Choose a point on the graph of any of these equations. *(You may have to demonstrate how to write the coordinates of a point.)* What does this point mean in terms of the problem? How does this point relate to the equations?

A point on a graph gives a pair of values for x and y (d and A) that, when substituted for x and y in the equation (function), produce a valid statement. In other words, the pair of values is a *solution* to the equation.

> In this problem, you will be asked to make sense of how a point on the graph and a pair of values that make the equation true are related.

Remind students to use their tables and graphs from Problem 2.3. As students have already constructed their tables and graphs, this problem should not take long. Have students think about the problem a few minutes individually and then confer in partners.

Explore

There are two questions that can be answered by locating the point (14, 2). If students have found only one, ask whether they can figure out the other. The essential understanding students should come to in this problem is that a point on a line is a solution to an equation.

Summarize

Ask students how they found their answers and why they make sense.

Assign the follow-up to be done in pairs. These questions ask students to use a graphing calculator. (If students do not have graphing calculators that can display a function in a table, modify these questions.) If students are struggling with the calculators, encourage them to help each other. You can also help as you circulate around the classroom.

Follow-up question 2 allows you to assess what your students remember and can do with a graphing calculator. If students are using a standard window, they will not be able to see the point on the graph using the trace feature. If so, question them about their window settings.

Why do you think your calculator is not showing values like those shown in your math book? *(The windows are different.)*

What might you do to produce a graph that would help you to answer this question? *(Reset the window to ranges for x and y that will show the part needed on the graph.)*

What quadrants are showing in the picture? How would you tell the calculator to show only those quadrants?

The picture shows only the first quadrant, so the minimum value of both x and y is 0.

After discussing follow-up questions 1 and 2, ask students to make up other specific equations that relate to the walkathon problem and to explain what question each equation is implying. The introduction to the investigation gives three different relationships; ask students to write specific equations for all three. For example:

- The equation $20 = 2d$ relates to Gilberto's plan and asks what distance a student would have to walk to collect $20.

- The equation $A = 5 + 0.5(24)$ relates to Alana's plan and asks what amount would be collected if a student walked 24 miles.

On the transparency or board version of the graph, have students indicate which points on the graph answer each question they propose.

3.2 • Graphing Lines

In this problem, students continue working with the ideas developed in Problem 3.1. Making graphs by hand, except for very simple equations, can be quite time-consuming. Using graphing calculators to make graphs makes many more problems accessible to students who understand the main concept, *a point on a graph represents a solution to an equation.* (This is such an important idea that you need to ask questions that lead students to this understanding again and again.) Any relationship that can be written as a function of *x* can be graphed on a graphing calculator, and each becomes the source for solutions to an infinite number of equations. Each time a value is substituted for the *x* or *y* variable, the graph can be traced to find the corresponding value of the other variable. The only inconvenience of the graphing calculator is that the window settings affect the output and must be adjusted to fit each equation.

Launch

Begin by discussing and having students experiment with the window settings on their graphing calculators. You may want to use the two windows and the equation that is graphed in the student edition; students can check their work against the illustrations. Ask questions about each window.

What is the range of values for the *x* variable? For the *y* variable? *(The x values range from 0 to 15 in window 1 and from ⁻10 to 10 in window 2. The y values range from ⁻4 to 15 in window 1 and from ⁻10 to 10 in window 2.)*

What is the scale, and what do you think it means on the graph? *(The scale for each variable on each graph is 1. This means that the tick marks on each axis represent 1 unit.)*

For each window, which of the four quadrants show on the screen? *(Quadrants I and IV are displayed on window 1 because the minimum value of x is 0. All four quadrants are displayed on window 2 because the values of x and y both range from negative to positive.)*

Give a window setting that will show only the first and second quadrants. *(Any setting with a minimum value for y that is greater than or equal to 0, and a range of x that includes positive and negative values, will display only quadrants I and II.)*

Do the tick marks on the *x*-axis and those on the *y*-axis represent the same value in windows 1 and 2? *(yes)*

Will the tick marks be the same distance apart on each axis? Why or why not? *(They will not be spaced the same because the range of values is different and because the viewing screen is a rectangle, not a square.)*

Have the class look at the question in the "Think about this!" It asks how far a student would have to walk to raise $8.50 from each sponsor under Alana's plan. Students should be able to

connect the point on the line with the solution for the related equation, $8.5 = 5 + 0.5x$. The point $(7, 8.5)$ lies on the line and satisfies the equation $y = 5 + 0.5x$; when y is 8.5, x is 7.

Have students try out different window settings for the equation until they are comfortable making sense of the values displayed at the bottom of the screen when the trace feature is used. You may need to remind them that in this problem, x represents d (distance walked) and y represents A (amount owed). Finding an appropriate window is similar to selecting an appropriate scale for paper-and-pencil graphs in that the range of values in which we are interested determines a sensible choice. Students should be aware of possible problems with window settings, though they do not have to master setting ranges at this time.

Explain that the trace feature will often not give whole-number coordinates; instead, it usually gives approximations. The approximations are sometimes useful as they are; exact values can be substituted back into the equations to see whether they work.

When your students seem comfortable setting a window and making a graph, pose the problem.

> In this problem, you will explore five equations using your graphing calculator. But first you are asked to get familiar with the equations by making a table for each without using your calculator. Then you will use your calculator to graph each equation. You are trying to find a way to tell what is happening to the value of the y variable as the x variable increases and to decide whether each equation represents a reasonable pledge plan for the walkathon.

Explore

If the class needs assistance getting started, you might look at equation i as a group.

> Enter $y = 3x$ and examine its graph. Is it increasing or decreasing from left to right? How did you decide?

If students' calculators can create tables, have students examine the table for this equation.

> Does the table help you decide whether the line is increasing or decreasing? Choose a pair of values from the table. Can you find that point in the graph? What specific equation goes with the point you chose? [For example, the point (2, 6) corresponds to the equation $6 = 3(2)$.]

Have students work on the problem individually, then compare answers and work on the follow-up with a partner. It is important that each student knows how to use the graphing calculator and can connect a solution for an equation with a particular point on a line. Troubleshoot while students are working. If several students are having problems, pair each with a student that is more adept with the graphing calculator.

As students work on the problem, suggest that they enter *one equation at a time* by first clearing the previous equation.

Summarize

Have students share their explanations about what each pledge plan means.

Which of these would not make a good pledge plan? Why?

Check students' solutions for parts B and C. Have them use the graphing calculator to generate a table (if their calculators have this feature) for one of the equations and to compare the calculator table with their paper-and-pencil tables from part B and their graphs from part C.

What relationship do you see between the tables and the graphs?

Wrap up the summary by discussing students' ideas for part D and the follow-up questions. Follow-up question 2 is asking students to think about order of operations.

3.3 • Finding Solutions

The equations from Problem 3.2 are revisited here, with a focus on finding solutions for given values of x or y. Students use the trace and table features of the graphing calculator to reason informally about the equations to find solutions. By using these features, students are able to read data pairs from graphs and tables. They encounter the issue of interpreting inconvenient calculator output, and they try different window settings. (Students are not expected to use symbolic methods at this time. Investigation 4 develops informal symbolic methods, which are made more formal in the grade 8 units.)

Launch

Review the introduction to the problem, which gives an example of an equation in general terms and two equations related to it that have a value of x or y substituted in the general equation.

Explain that students will be solving to find pairs of related values for the same equations they explored in Problem 3.2. Put students in groups of two or three to work on the problem. Save the follow-up questions for the summary.

Explore

Your main role in this exploration will be helping students to make sense of what is being asked in each part of the problem. If students are having trouble, remind them that they made a table and graph for each equation in Problem 3.2.

Summarize

Have students share their solutions and strategies for each part of the problem. Ask for explanations. Students should be making the connection between solutions to specific equations and points that lie on the graph of the general equation. They should see the relationship among such equations, as in the following:

$$y = 5x - 3 \text{ is related to } 10 = 5x - 3, \ ^-6 = 5x - 3, \text{ and } y = 5(2) - 3$$

Wrap up the problem by having groups of students challenge each other by *writing an equation that can be solved from one of the given relationships.* For example, the graph of the equation $y = 2x + 3$ can be traced to find solutions to $8 = 2x + 3$ or $^-4 = 2x + 3$. A group could give one of these to another group and ask that they choose the correct line to graph, trace the line to the solution, and interpret the output.

Write the following equations on the board:

$$16 = 5x + 1 \qquad\qquad y = 2(4) + 6$$

What equation would you graph to find the solution to these equations?

When students seem to understand the process, have them do the follow-up questions individually and then discuss them. This will serve as a check on their understanding and give them in-class practice with the concepts.

For the Teacher: Graphing Straight Lines

The graphing calculator is a great tool for exploring families of lines or the effect of changing the slope or the *y*-intercept. Students can deepen their understanding of constant rates and the *y*-intercept by using the graphing calculator to investigate problems such as the following.

> *Problem 1:* Investigate equations of the form $y = mx$. Substitute values for *m*, and graph each equation. What can you say about *m*?

Students might observe several patterns:

- All the lines pass through the origin (have a *y*-intercept of 0).
- If *m* is positive, the line increases from left to right.
- The greater the slope, the steeper the line.
- If *m* is negative, the line decreases from left to right.
- If *m* is 0, the line is horizontal.

> *Problem 2:* Investigate lines of the form $y = x + b$. Substitute values for *b* into the equation, and graph each line.

Students might observe these patterns:

- The lines are all parallel to each other, and they all have a slope of 1.
- The lines are parallel to the line $y = x$. If *b* is positive, the line $y = x$ moves *b* units up; if *b* is negative, the line $y = x$ moves *b* units down.

3.4 • Planning a Skating Party

In this problem, students find a common solution to two equations.

Launch

This launch has two parts. The first part, an introductory activity using the results of Problem 2.5, will help students find an appropriate viewing window to locate the point of intersection of two lines on a graphing calculator. In their previous work with windows, students should have come to understand that they must be careful when interpreting the output of the graphing calculator. Making a sensible choice for the window settings is a skill that is developed over time.

Part 1: Finding the Appropriate Viewing Window and Points of Intersection

Display the graphs of the equations from Problem 2.5, which represent the distances Emile ($d = 2.5t$) and Henri ($d = t + 45$) are from the starting line.

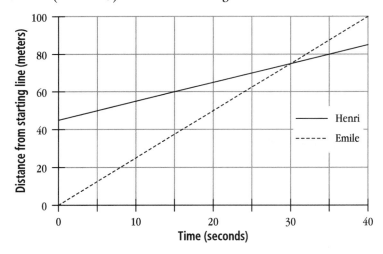

What information does the point of intersection of the two graphs represent?

The point of intersection is the point at which Emile overtakes Henri. The boys will be the *same distance* from the starting line and will have walked the *same amount of time.*

What are the coordinates of the point of intersection? *(The intersection occurs at t = 30 seconds and d = 75 meters.)*

How did you find the point of intersection?

Students will have found this in Problem 2.5 by making a graph by hand.

Explain that this point can also be found by using a graphing calculator. Enter the equations into your overhead graphing calculator (if you have one), and have students do the same. So that everyone has the same equations for Y_1 and Y_2, have them enter the following:

- Henri's equation, $d = 45 + t$, becomes $Y_1 = X + 45$

- Emile's equation, $d = 2.5t$, becomes $Y_2 = 2.5X$.

Y_1 is the distance Henri is from the starting line after x seconds; Y_2 is the distance Emile is from the starting line after x seconds.

If the standard viewing window is used, the graph of Y_1 may not show up because the range will be too narrow. Talk with students about what might be a more appropriate range for the graphs of these equations. Suggest that they use the table of values that they generated for Problem 2.5 as a guide for choosing the range of values for x and y. For example, the range for x might be from 0 to 40 with a scale of 2 or 4, and the range for y might be from 0 to 100 with a scale of 5 or 10.

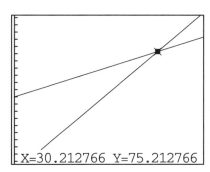

X=30.212766 Y=75.212766

Using the trace feature alone does not usually produce an exact answer. You can use the process outlined in the last problem to redefine the range of values for x and y in order to get a more precise result from the trace feature. For example, x is close to 30, so try a range of 25 to 35 and a scale of 1 for x. As y is close to 70, try a range of 70 to 80 and a scale of 1 for y.

The table feature gives accuracy more quickly. As discussed earlier, the graphs often give approximate values, and better approximations can be obtained by adjusting the viewing window. However, many students find tables quicker and easier to adjust to get more precision. Either approach is fine.

Another useful method for finding the point of intersection on the TI-82 calculator is using the $\boxed{\text{CALC}}$ key. The $\boxed{\text{CALC}}$ key has an "intersection" option. When this option is selected, the calculator automatically reads the intersection point.

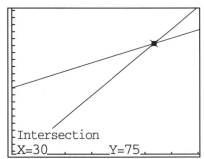

Once students have graphed the equations, continue with the discussion. (Some students may use tables, which also work.)

> Find the point on the graphs when Emile overtakes Henri. How can you be sure on a calculator that this point is on both lines?
>
> How does the point of intersection you found compare to the answer you obtained in Problem 2.5 using the graph you drew by hand?
>
> How far is each person from the starting line after 40 seconds? After 60 seconds? You may need to adjust the ranges on your calculator to find these.
>
> If Henri walks so that he is 100 meters from the starting line, how far will Emile walk in that same amount of time?

You may want to give students other equations, such as $Y_1 = 10X - 15$ and $Y_2 = 25 - 3X$, to offer them more practice finding appropriate window settings.

> Enter both equations, and adjust the window. Look for some points on the lines. Find the point of intersection.

You can use these problems to more formally introduce the x- and y-intercepts and the coefficient of x. Students have been talking about these concepts but may have been using imprecise language to express their ideas. In this problem, we will establish the more formal mathematical language. Discuss the significance of the x- and y-intercepts and the coefficient of x in the distance equations for Emile and Henri.

Part 2: Introducing Problem 3.4

In this problem, much of the knowledge that students have been building is stated formally. From Investigation 2, students know how rates are connected to the coefficient of the independent variable. They are familiar with the effects that rates have on graphs, tables, and equations.

From their work in Problems 3.1 and 3.2, they know how to use a graph and a table to solve an equation. Now they will use a graph to find a solution common to two linear equations.

The $y = mx + b$ form of a linear equation is presented in the introduction to the problem in the student edition. Because students have already explored the effect of different rates on graphs, tables, and equations, the significance of m should be familiar to them. They will also consider the effect of the constant term b on graphs and tables. The particular data pair that gives the y-intercept is emphasized as well. It is just another solution from the many that are represented on a graph and in a table, but it has particular importance—in this case, in terms of the skate-rental costs.

Continue the discussion from part 1 of the launch. Read and discuss the introduction to Problem 3.4. Help students to use the vocabulary—*coefficient* and *y-intercept*—to express their ideas. You may want to offer two or three additional examples to help them understand why b in the equation $y = mx + b$ is the y-intercept. This would also be a good time to use some of the equations from previous problems to clarify the meaning of the y-intercept and the coefficient of x.

> **What information does *m* represent?** *(It indicates the steepness of the line—whether it is increasing, decreasing, or remaining the same.)*
>
> **What impact do you think *b* has on the appearance of the line?**
> *(It indicates the point at which the line crosses the y-axis.)*

If students reply that it moves the line up or down, you may need to ask the following questions:

> **What does the graph of *y = x* look like? What does the graph of *y = x* + 2 look like?**
>
> **How are the two graphs related? Can this relationship be predicted from looking at the equations?**
>
> **What would the graphs of *y = x* + 5 and *y = x* – 1 look like?**

Discuss briefly that the form $y = mx + b$ is a general form of a linear equation. All the linear situations that students have studied so far fit this form—only the values of m and b have changed.

Introduce the story of the skating party, and let students work in pairs on the problem.

Explore

Keep an eye out for students who are having trouble using the calculator and the trace feature. By the end of this activity, all students should be able to use the calculator to graph and trace with some confidence. Have students who have caught on well work with those who are still struggling.

Summarize

Have students share their answers to the problem and discuss their strategies. In addition to graphing the two equations, students may have used strategies such as guess and check. These additional strategies will complement the usual method. It is important that students discuss a

variety of ways of answering the question and that they have an opportunity to make sense of the problem in their own way.

Use the follow-up as part of the summary, posing the questions one at a time and having students share their thinking. After students have worked on follow-up question 1, ask the following questions:

> How did you determine your equations?
>
> When you graphed your equations, what range of values did you use? Why is your range reasonable? Did anyone use a different range? Why did you choose those values for your range?
>
> How is this problem similar to Problem 2.5, which was about Henri and Emile's walking race?

Help students to see that the cost per person in this problem is similar to the rate at which each boy walked and that this rate affects the steepness of the lines. The fixed cost for Wheelie's Skates and Stuff is similar to the head start that Henri received, and both are represented by the y-intercept.

In question 2, if students have slightly different approximations for the point of intersection, explore how a more accurate answer can be found by adjusting the window or using a table. Explain to students that they should always check the reasonableness of their answers in the context of the problem. They can also substitute their answers into the equations to see whether they are approximately correct.

Additional Answers

Answers to Problem 3.2

A. i.   The participant earns $3 for each mile walked.

ii. The participant loses $2 for each mile walked.

iii. The participant earns $5 for each mile walked minus a $3 fee.

iv. The participant gets a $6 donation and then loses $1 for each mile walked.

v.   The participant gets a $2 donation (the number of miles walked has no effect on how much is collected).

B. i.   The plan is reasonable, as the participant would collect money for each mile walked.

x	y
1	3
2	6
3	9
4	12
5	15

ii. The plan is unreasonable, as the participant would lose money for each mile walked.

x	y
1	-2
2	-4
3	-6
4	-8
5	-10

iii. The plan might be considered reasonable. The participant would have to pay an initial fee of $3, which would be covered as long as he or she walked at least 1 mile. The participant continues to make money for each mile walked.

x	y
1	2
2	7
3	12
4	17
5	22

iv. The plan would probably be considered unreasonable. After earning a $6 donation, the participant would lose money for each mile walked. With this plan, the most profitable course of action would be not to walk at all.

x	y
1	5
2	4
3	3
4	2
5	1

v. The plan might be considered reasonable if the participant was not concerned about collecting more for walking more. The participant would collect no more than the initial $2.

x	y
1	2
2	2
3	2
4	2
5	2

C. Graphs will vary, depending on the scale used.

i.

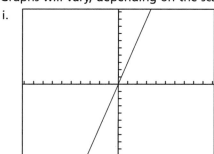

ii.

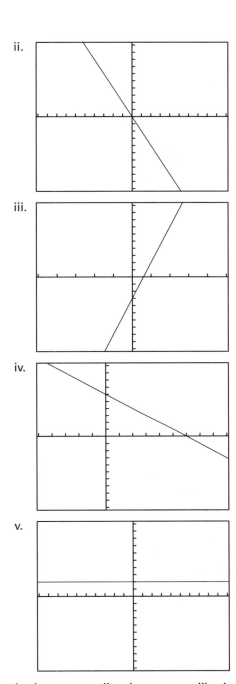

iii.

iv.

v.

D. i. increase   ii. decrease   iii. increase   iv. decrease   v. stay the same

From the graph, you can tell that the y values are increasing if the graph rises from left to right and decreasing if the graph falls from left to right. If the graph is a horizontal line, y is constant and is not increasing or decreasing. *From the table,* you can look at the values in the y column. If they are increasing, y is increasing. If they are decreasing, y is decreasing. If every y value is the same, y is constant. *From the equation,* you can tell how y is changing by looking at the coefficient of x. If it is positive, y will increase as x increases. If it is negative, y will decrease as x increases. If it is 0 (a rule of the form $y = b$), y is a constant value no matter what the value of x is. (Note: If students use the trace feature, they can read the y values and observe whether they are increasing or decreasing. If they use the table feature, they can scroll down the table and observe the change in the y values. It may be difficult for students to tell from the equation whether the y values are increasing. However, they may notice that when the number that x is multiplied by is negative, the y values decrease.)

Answers to Problem 3.2 Follow-Up

2. Tamara has added $^-3$ and 5 to get 2 and then multiplied by $^-1$. Ali's answer is correct, because he multiplied $^-1$ by 5 to get $^-5$ and then added $^-3$. (Note: In mathematics, we must agree on how we will perform the steps in a calculation. Ali's interpretation is the one mathematicians have agreed to use: multiplication is done before addition. The concept of order of operations is raised informally several times in the Connected Mathematics program, allowing students' understanding to grow over time. In the grade 8 unit *Say It with Symbols,* students encounter a more formal development of order of operations.)

Answers to Problem 3.3

A. 1. equation iii, $y = 5x - 3$

   2. $x = ^-1$

B. 1. equation ii, $y = ^-2x$

   2. $x = ^-3.4$

X	Y₁
$^-3.8$	7.6
$^-3.7$	7.4
$^-3.6$	7.2
$^-3.5$	7
$^-3.4$	6.8
$^-3.3$	6.6
X = $^-3.4$	

C. Possible answer: For $^-8 = 5x - 3$, I thought about the equation as "What number can I multiply by 5, and then subtract 3 from, to get an answer of $^-8$?" I noticed that the number had to be negative, because when 3 is subtracted from the product, the answer would be negative. I tried a couple of numbers and found that $^-1 \times 5 = ^-5$, and $^-5 - 3 = ^-8$. For $6.8 = ^-2x$, I thought about what I could multiply by $^-2$ to get 6.8, and that's half of 6.8, or 3.4. (Note: Students may start to work through the problem backward—a concept introduced in Investigation 4—and should be encouraged to try their equations in this way if they come up with that approach. For example: The number 3 is subtracted so I must add 3 to $^-8$ to get $^-5$. Now $^-5$ equals 5 times x, so I must undo the multiplication by dividing by 5: $\frac{^-5}{5} = \frac{5x}{5}$ or $^-1 = x$.)

D. 1. Because $x = ^-1$ is a solution to the equation $^-8 = 5x - 3$, the coordinate pair $(^-1, ^-8)$ fits the equation $y = 5x - 3$.

   2. Possible answer: $(0, ^-3)$, $(4, 17)$, and $(^-4, ^-23)$; Each can be shown to fit the equation by replacing x in the equation with the first number (the x value) and solving the expression. The result will be the second number (the y value).

Answers to Problem 3.3 Follow-Up

3. a. Possible answer: $12 = ^-3x + 6$, $4 = ^-3x + 6$, $^-6 = ^-3x + 6$

   b. The solution to $12 = ^-3x + 6$ is $x = ^-2$ and $y = 12$. The solution to $4 = ^-3x + 6$ is $x = \frac{2}{3}$ and $y = 4$. The solution to $^-6 = ^-3x + 6$ is $x = 4$ and $y = ^-6$.

c.

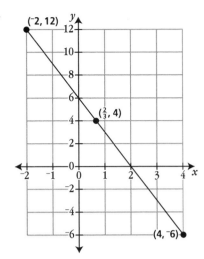

(-2, 12)

$(\frac{2}{3}, 4)$

(4, -6)

d. Students should be able to use their graphing calculators to graph the line for $y = {}^-3x + 6$ and trace along the line to locate their three pairs of values. They might explain that they know they are correct because the trace feature gave coordinate values that were very close to what they had.

Answers to Problem 3.4 Follow-Up

1. a. Roll-Away Skates: $y = 5x$, Wheelie's Skates and Stuff: $y = 3x + 100$

   b.

   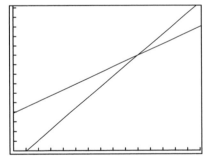

   c. Possible answer: $x = 0$ to 75 and $y = 0$ to 350 (Note: Students should use a range that allows them to see the intersection of the lines.)

2. a. Point (8, 40) is on the graph of $y = 5x$ (Roll-Away Skates). If 8 people rent skates, this company will charge $40.

   b. Point (8, 124) is on the graph of $y = 3x + 100$ (Wheelie's). If 8 people rent skates, this company will charge $124.

   c. The point of intersection is (50, 250); it is on both graphs. If 50 people rent skates, both companies will charge $250.

3. a. The y-intercept of $y = 5x$ is (0, 0), and the y-intercept of $y = 100 + 3x$ is (0, 100).

   b. In $y = 5x$, the y-intercept means that when the number of people renting skates is 0, the cost is $0. In $y = 100 + 3x$, it means that when the number of people renting skates is 0, the cost is $100.

   c. These are the points where the lines cross the y-axis.

   d. The y-intercepts are the points where the number of people renting skates (the x value) is 0.

4. The coefficient of x in $y = 5x$ is 5; the coefficient of x in $y = 3x + 100$ is 3. These coefficients are the rate per person to rent skates. The coefficient of x affects the steepness of the graph.

5. For 100 students, Roll-Away Skates would charge $500 and Wheelie's would charge $400, so Wheelie's would be the better deal.

6. For $250, you could rent 50 pairs of skates from either Roll-Away Skates or Wheelie's.

ACE Answers

Applications

1a.

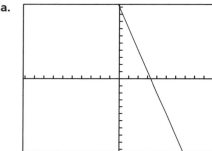

2a.

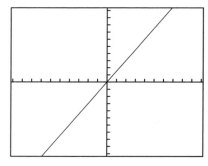

3a.

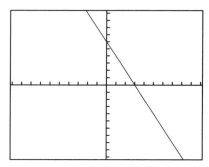

4a.

9a. Possible answer: *x* values from ⁻8 to 2, *y* values from ⁻2 to 10

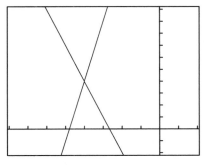

10a. Possible answer: *x* values from 2 to 10, *y* values from ⁻6 to 3

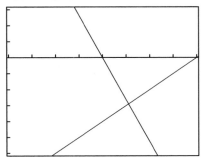

11a. Possible answer: *x* values from ⁻3 to 2, *y* values from 6 to 12

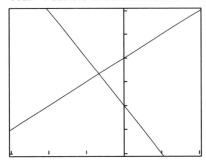

12a. Possible answer: *x* values from ⁻1 to 4, *y* values from 3 to 10

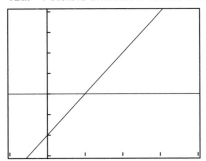

16c.

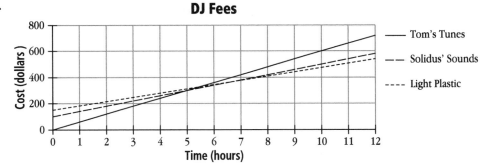

DJ Fees

Tom's Tunes
Solidus' Sounds
Light Plastic

Solving Equations

In this investigation, students develop ways to solve equations of the form $y = mx + b$ symbolically. In Problem 4.1, Paying in Installments, students consider a problem in which merchandise is bought on an installment plan and solve the problem in any way they choose. The situation is revisited in Problem 4.2, Using the Symbolic Method, in which students investigate building the related equation and then "undoing" each operation to solve for a particular value. Students then write and solve a similar equation using the symbolic method. Additional practice of the technique is provided in the follow-up to the problem. Problem 4.3, Analyzing Bones, is an interesting application problem involving real data. Students use equations from forensic science to estimate the lengths of human bones.

Mathematical and Problem-Solving Goals

- **To solve an equation of the form $y = mx + b$ symbolically**

- **To connect various methods of finding information in graphs and in tables and by solving equations**

Materials		
Problem	**For students**	**For the teacher**
All	Graphing calculators	Transparencies 4.1 to 4.3 (optional), transparent grids (optional; copy the grids onto transparency film), overhead display model of students' graphing calculator (optional)
4.3	Blank transparencies or large sheets of paper (optional), rulers or tape measures	

INVESTIGATION

Solving Equations

In previous investigations, you answered questions about linear relationships by using graphs and tables and by reasoning about the numbers involved. In this investigation, you will learn how to answer such questions by writing and solving linear equations.

4.1 Paying in Installments

The Unlimited Store allows any customer who buys merchandise costing over $30 to pay on an installment plan. The customer pays $30 down and then pays $15 a month until the item is paid for.

Problem 4.1

Suppose you buy a $195 CD-ROM drive from the Unlimited Store on an installment plan. How many months will it take you to pay for the drive? Describe how you found your answer.

▨ Problem 4.1 Follow-Up

1. Write down the sequence of steps you used to find the solution to Problem 4.1. Try to use mathematical symbols and not just words to describe your steps.
2. Make up a problem similar to Problem 4.1, and solve it using your method from question 1.

Launch

- Pose the problem of buying on an installment plan.
- Let pairs solve the problem any way they choose.

Explore

- As pairs work, ask questions about how they are thinking about the problem.
- Ask students to write down how they solved the problem.
- Have pairs work on the follow-up (or, wait after the summary of the problem).

Summarize

- Let students share their solutions, and help them make connections among the methods used.
- Have the class write an equation to represent the problem and use a graphing calculator to analyze it. *(optional)*
- Review the problems students created for the follow-up.

Answer to Problem 4.1

Possible answer: As 195 − 30 = 165, there is $165 remaining to pay. At $15 a month, it will take 165 ÷ 15 = 11 months to pay off the item. (Note: Students may use various methods to arrive at their answers, including tables and graphs. If students use a graphing calculator, their answers may be approximate.)

Answers to Problem 4.1 Follow-Up

1. Possible answer: The cost is $195 and the down payment is $30: 195 − 30 = 165. So, this is the amount still owed: 165. At $15 a month, this is how long it will take to pay off the item: 165 ÷ 15 = 11 months.
2. Students may write a problem similar to the installment-plan problem. Some may use their own experience of buying something on time.

Assignment Choices

ACE questions 1–3, 11, 13, 16, and unassigned choices from earlier problems (16 is particularly difficult)

Using the Symbolic Method

At a Glance

Grouping:
groups of 2 or 3

Launch

- Introduce the method of solving an equation symbolically by undoing the operations.

- Talk about the stove bought on the installment plan.

- Work through a simplified problem. *(optional)*

Explore

- As groups work, ask about how they are thinking.

Summarize

- Have students demonstrate their symbolic methods as the class verifies each step.

- Ask questions to make sure students understand the method.

- Demonstrate the equivalence between undoing the operations and balancing the equation.

- Have students work on the follow-up, then review it.

Assignment Choices

ACE questions 4–8, 12, and unassigned choices from earlier problems (4–6 require a graphing calculator)

4.2 Using the Symbolic Method

The students in your class may have found several ways to solve Problem 4.1. Some may have used a table or a graph. Others may have found a way to reason about the quantities in the problem. For example, in Ms. Winslow's class, one student reasoned as follows:

"If I pay $30 down, I will have $195 − $30, or $165, left to pay. If I pay $15 a month, then it will take me $165 ÷ 15 = 11, months to pay for the drive."

You can also solve Problem 4.1 by writing and solving an equation. To write an equation, you could reason as follows:

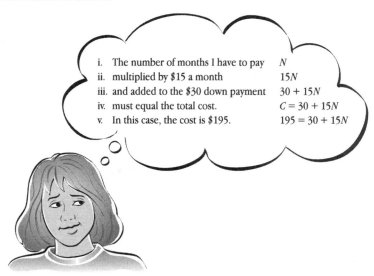

i.   The number of months I have to pay N
ii. multiplied by $15 a month $15N$
iii. and added to the $30 down payment $30 + 15N$
iv. must equal the total cost. $C = 30 + 15N$
v.   In this case, the cost is $195. $195 = 30 + 15N$

To find the number of months you must pay, you need to find the value of N that makes the equation $195 = 30 + 15N$ a true statement. This is called *solving the equation* for the variable N.

From your work in the last investigation, you know you can solve $195 = 30 + 15N$ by making a table or a graph of the general equation $C = 30 + 15N$. Now you will learn to solve $195 = 30 + 15N$ by *operating on the symbols* in the equation.

Thinking	Manipulating the Symbols
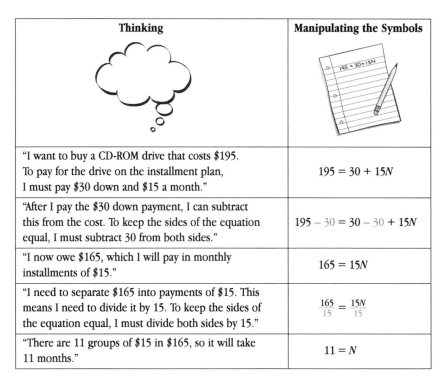	
"I want to buy a CD-ROM drive that costs $195. To pay for the drive on the installment plan, I must pay $30 down and $15 a month."	$195 = 30 + 15N$
"After I pay the $30 down payment, I can subtract this from the cost. To keep the sides of the equation equal, I must subtract 30 from both sides."	$195 - 30 = 30 - 30 + 15N$
"I now owe $165, which I will pay in monthly installments of $15."	$165 = 15N$
"I need to separate $165 into payments of $15. This means I need to divide it by 15. To keep the sides of the equation equal, I must divide both sides by 15."	$\frac{165}{15} = \frac{15N}{15}$
"There are 11 groups of $15 in $165, so it will take 11 months."	$11 = N$

After you solve an equation, you should always check your solution by substituting it back into the original equation. Here are the steps you would follow to check the solution to the equation above.

$$195 = 30 + 15N$$
$$195 = 30 + 15(11)$$
$$195 = 30 + 165$$
$$195 = 195$$

Review the table above. The strategy we used to solve the equation was to *undo,* or *reverse,* the operations until the variable was alone on one side of the equation. Notice that we applied each reverse operation to *both* sides of the equation. We will refer to this strategy for solving an equation as the *symbolic method.*

Problem 4.2

Karen wants to buy a stove from the Unlimited Store on an installment plan. The stove costs $305.

A. Write an equation you could solve to find the number of months it will take Karen to pay for the stove.

B. Solve your equation by using the symbolic method. How many months will it take Karen to pay for the stove?

■ **Problem 4.2 Follow-Up**

1. In a–d, use the symbolic method to solve the equation for x. Check your answers.
  a. $y = 2.5x$ when $y = 175$
  b. $y = 19 + 3x$ when $y = 64$
  c. $y = 2x - 50$ when $y = 15$
  d. $y = {}^-2x + 14$ when $y = 60$

2. What other methods could you use to solve for x in the equations in question 1?

Answers to Problem 4.2

A. $305 = 30 + 15N$, where N is the number of months to pay off the stove

B. $N = 18\frac{1}{3}$ (19 months is an acceptable answer)

Answers to Problem 4.2 Follow-Up

1. See page 63h.

2. Answers will vary. Students may choose to look at a graph or a table to help them answer this question.

4.3 Analyzing Bones

Forensic scientists can estimate a person's height by measuring the length of certain bones, including the femur, the tibia, the humerus, and the radius.

The table below gives equations for the relationships between the length of each bone and the height for males and females. These relationships were found by scientists after much study and data collection. In the table, F represents the length of the femur, T the length of the tibia, H the length of the humerus, R the length of the radius, and h the person's height. All measurements are in centimeters.

— Humerus (H)

— Radius (R)

— Femur (F)

— Tibia (T)

Bone	Male	Female
Femur	$h = 69.089 + 2.238F$	$h = 61.412 + 2.317F$
Tibia	$h = 81.688 + 2.392T$	$h = 72.572 + 2.533T$
Humerus	$h = 73.570 + 2.970H$	$h = 64.977 + 3.144H$
Radius	$h = 80.405 + 3.650R$	$h = 73.502 + 3.876R$

Source: George Knill. "Mathematics in Forensic Science." *Mathematics Teacher* (February 1981): 31–32.

Problem 4.3

Use the equations on page 57 to answer parts A–D.

A. How tall is a female if her femur is 46.2 centimeters long?

B. How tall is a male if his tibia is 50.1 centimeters long?

C. If a woman is 152 centimeters (about 5 feet) tall, how long is her femur? Her tibia? Her humerus? Her radius?

D. If a man is 183 centimeters (about 6 feet) tall, how long is his femur? His tibia? His humerus? His radius?

■ Problem 4.3 Follow-Up

For one of the bones discussed above, graph the equations for males and females on the same set of axes. What do the x- and y-intercepts represent in terms of this problem? Does this make sense? Why?

Analyzing Bones

At a Glance

Grouping: groups of 2 or 3

Launch

■ Introduce the forensics information, and ask questions to make sure students understand what information each equation can give.

Explore

■ Give groups transparencies or large sheets of paper for recording answers. *(optional)*

■ Ask groups who finish early to try to measure their own bone lengths and their heights to test the equations.

■ Have students do the follow-up individually and then share answers in groups.

Summarize

■ Have students share their work and thinking for each part of the problem.

■ Ask several students to share their graph from the follow-up and explain what the x- and y-intercepts mean.

Answers to Problem 4.3

A. $h = 61.412 + 2.317(46.2) = 168.5$ cm

B. $h = 81.688 + 2.392(50.1) = 201.5$ cm

C. See page 63h.

D. See page 63h.

Answer to Problem 4.3 Follow-Up

Graphs will vary. The x-intercept tells the value for x (femur, tibia, humerus, or radius length) when the height of the person is 0, and the y-intercept tells the value for y (the person's height) when the length of a bone is 0. These values do not make sense in the context of the problem.

Assignment Choices

ACE questions 9, 10, 14, 15, 17, and unassigned choices from earlier problems (17 is particularly difficult)

Did you know?

Forensic scientists use scientific methods to solve crimes. Today, fingerprints and DNA evidence are used to identify criminals, but early forensic scientists used methods based on body measurements. Beginning in 1879, the Bertillon system—developed by the French criminologist Dr. Alphonse Bertillon—was used to identify criminals and suspects. The Bertillon system involves measuring characteristics that do not change as a person ages. The system first classifies a person as having a short, medium, or long head. Similar divisions are then made based on the length of the middle finger, the length of the forearm, the length of the little finger, and height. Final subdivisions are made according to eye color and ear length. Many criminals underwent surgical procedures to escape their Bertillon classifications.

Tips for the Linguistically Diverse Classroom

Rebus Scenario The Rebus Scenario technique is described in detail in *Getting to Know Connected Mathematics*. This technique involves sketching rebuses on the chalkboard that correspond to key words in the story or information that you present orally. Example: Some key words and phrases for which you may need to draw rebuses while discussing the "Did you know?" feature are *fingerprints* (a thumbprint), *criminal* (stick-figure bandit), *short, medium, or long head* (heads of three sizes), *length of the middle finger* (finger next to a ruler), *surgical procedures* (stick-figure bandit lying on a table while stick-figure doctor operates).

As you work on these ACE questions, use your calculator whenever you need it.

Applications

1. Find x if $326 = 4x$.

2. Find p if $93 = 16 - 5p$.

3. Find n if $321.5 = 16n - 25.5$.

In 4–6, do parts a and b by using the symbolic method and by using a graphing calculator.

4. $y = x - 15$
   a. Find y if $x = 9.4$.   b. Find x if $y = 29$.

5. $y = 10 - 2.5x$
   a. Find y if $x = 3.2$.   b. Find x if $y = 85$.

6. $y = 5x - 15$
   a. Find y if $x = 1$.   b. Find x if $y = 50$.

7. In questions 4–6, you solved linear equations by using the symbolic method and by using a graphing calculator. Compare these two methods. Which do you prefer? Why?

8. Below is a student's solution to the equation $58.5 = 3.5x - 6$. The student made an error. Find the error, and give the correct solution.

$$58.5 = 3.5x - 6$$
$$58.5 - 6 = 3.5x$$
$$52.5 = 3.5x$$
$$\frac{52.5}{3.5} = x$$
$$\text{so } 15 = x$$

Investigation 4: Solving Equations   59

3.
$$321.5 = 16n - 25.5$$
$$321.5 + 25.5 = 16n - 25.5 + 25.5$$
$$347 = 16n$$
$$\frac{347}{16} = \frac{16n}{16}$$
$$21.6875 = n$$

5a. $y = 10 - 2.5x$
$$y = 10 - 2.5(3.2)$$
$$y = 2$$

5b.
$$y = 10 - 2.5x$$
$$85 = 10 - 2.5x$$
$$85 - 10 = 10 - 10 - 2.5x$$
$$75 = ^-2.5x$$
$$\frac{75}{^-2.5} = \frac{^-2.5x}{^-2.5}$$
$$^-30 = x$$

6a. $y = 5x - 15$
$$y = 5(1) - 15$$
$$y = ^-10$$

6b.
$$y = 5x - 15$$
$$50 = 5x - 15$$
$$50 + 15 = 5x - 15 + 15$$
$$65 = 5x$$
$$\frac{65}{5} = \frac{5x}{5}$$
$$13 = x$$

Answers

Applications

1. $326 = 4x$
   $\frac{326}{4} = \frac{4x}{4}$
   $81.5 = x$

2. $93 = 16 - 5p$
   $93 - 16 = 16 - 16 - 5p$
   $77 = ^-5p$
   $\frac{77}{^-5} = \frac{^-5p}{^-5}$
   $^-15.4 = p$

3. See below left.

4a. $y = x - 15$
   $y = 9.4 - 15$
   $y = ^-5.6$

4b. $y = x - 15$
   $29 = x - 15$
   $29 + 15 = x - 15 + 15$
   $44 = x$

5. See below left.

6. See below left.

7. Solving these equations using a graphing calculator can be problematic. First, students have to determine appropriate windows for viewing the graph, windows that show the necessary range of x and y values. Second, the trace feature will not necessarily display the desired values for x and y, but only an approximation. It is hoped that students will express some appreciation for the efficiency of the symbolic method. While it is important not to imply that one method should be used over another, students should come to their own conclusions about the symbolic method and its advantages in finding solutions.

8. The first step is incorrect. The student should have reversed the operation of subtracting 6 by adding 6. The correct answer is $64.5 \div 3.5 =$ about 18.43.

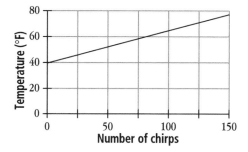

9a. $n = 4(60) - 160 =$ 80 chirps

9b. $t = \frac{150}{4} + 40 = 77.5°F$

9c. This would be when the number of chirps is 0: $t = \frac{0}{4} + 40 = 40°F$.

9d. See below right.

10a. $C = 800 + 3.20(100) =$ $\$1120$, $R = 8.50(100) =$ $\$850$; Fabian did not make a profit; he lost $\$270$.

10b. $1105 = 8.50N$, so $N = 130$ cakes

10c. $C = 800 + 3.20(130) =$ $\$1216$

10d. See page 63i.

10e. In the cost equation, the y-intercept gives the cost when 0 cakes are produced. The coefficient of N gives the cost for making and selling each cake. In the revenue equation, the y-intercept gives the revenue for selling 0 cakes. The coefficient of N shows the revenue for each cake sold.

---

9. The number of times a cricket chirps in a minute is a function of the temperature. You can use the formula

$$n = 4t - 160$$

to determine the number of chirps, n, a cricket makes in a minute when the temperature is t degrees Fahrenheit. If you want to estimate the temperature by counting cricket chirps, it is easier to use the following form of the equation:

$$t = \frac{1}{4}n + 40$$

a. At 60°F, how many times does a cricket chirp in a minute?

b. What is the temperature if a cricket chirps 150 times in a minute?

c. At what temperature does a cricket stop chirping?

d. Sketch a graph of the equation with number of chirps on the x-axis and temperature on the y-axis. What information does the y-intercept give you?

10. At Fabulous Fabian's Bakery, the cost, C, and revenue, R, to make and sell N cakes per month are given by the equations below.

$$C = 800 + 3.20N \qquad \text{and} \qquad R = 8.50N$$

a. Fabian sold 100 cakes in January. What were his cost and his revenue? Did he make a profit?

b. In April, Fabian's revenue was $\$1105$. How many cakes did he sell?

c. What was the cost of producing the number of cakes from part b?

d. What is the break-even point between cost and revenue?

e. In each equation, what information do the y-intercept and the coefficient of N give you?

9d. The y-intercept gives the temperature when the number of chirps is 0. (Note: An interesting question to raise is, If the graph were extended to the left, what meaning would that part have?)

11. In a and b, find the mystery number, and explain your reasoning.

    a. If you add 15 to 3 times this mystery number, you get 78. What is the mystery number?

    b. If you subtract 27 from 5 times this mystery number, you get 83. What is the mystery number?

    c. Make up clues for a riddle whose answer is 9.

Connections

12. When a person reaches the age of 30, his or her height starts decreasing by approximately 0.06 centimeter per year.

    a. If a basketball player is 6 feet, 6 inches tall on his thirtieth birthday, about how tall will he be at age 80? (Remember, 1 inch ≈ 2.5 centimeters.)

    b. Myron's 80-year-old grandmother is 160 centimeters tall. About how tall was she at age 30?

13. World Connections long-distance phone company charges $50 a month plus 10¢ a minute for each call.

    a. Write an equation for the total monthly cost, C, for m minutes of long-distance calls.

    b. A customer made $10\frac{1}{2}$ hours of long-distance calls in a month. How much was his bill for that month?

    c. A customer received a $75 long-distance bill for last month's calls. How many minutes of long-distance calls did she make?

    d. The International Links long-distance phone company has no monthly fee and charges 18¢ a minute for long-distance calls. Compare the World Connections long-distance plan to the International Links plan. Under what circumstances is it cheaper to use International Links?

13d. Students may look at a graph or table of the relationships $C = 50 + 0.10m$ and $C = 0.18m$ to determine that International Links would be cheaper unless the customer talks more than 625 min per month. The table shows that the two equations have equal values when $x = 625$ and that International Links (Y_2), charging 18¢ per minute, is less expensive for all values of x less than 625.

X	Y₁	Y₂
525	102.5	94.5
550	105	99
575	107.5	103.5
600	110	108
625	112.5	112.5
650	115	117
675	117.5	121.5

X = 625

11a. Since 78 − 15 = 63, 3 times the mystery number is 63, so the mystery number is 21.

11b. Since 83 + 27 = 110, and 110 ÷ 5 = 22, the mystery number is 22.

11c. Answers will vary. (Note: You may want to encourage a discussion about how students developed their riddles, such as whether they worked backward from the answer of 9 or forward in trying to get 9 as an answer.)

Connections

12a. Since 1 in ≈ 2.5 cm, 6 ft 6 in is 195 cm. At 80, the basketball player will have lost 50 × 0.06 = 3 cm, and his height will be 195 − 3 = 192 cm (a little under 6 ft 5 in). This could be written as $h = 195 − 0.06n$, where h is the height at some future time and n is the number of years beyond age 30.

12b. At 80, she will have lost 50 × 0.06 = 3 cm, so she must have been 163 cm tall at age 30. The symbolic statement is $160 = t − 0.06(50)$, where t is the height at 30.

13a. $C = 50 + 0.10m$

13b. $10\frac{1}{2}$ h = 630 min, so $C = 50 + 0.10(630) = \$113$

13c. $75 = 50 + 0.10m$, so $m = 250$ min

13d. See left.

14. The circumference rule $C = 2\pi r$ represents a linear relationship; the area rule $A = \pi r^2$ does not.

15a. $d = 50t$

15b. $20 = rt$ or $t = \frac{20}{r}$

15c. The equation in part a is linear; the equation in part b is not. (Note: Students can use graphing calculators to confirm that the graph and table for the equation in part b are not typical of a linear relationship.)

Extensions

16a. $C = 0.55 + 0.23(10 - 1) = \$2.62$

16b. See page 63i.

16c. $C = 0.55 + 0.23(m - 1)$

17a. See below right.

17b. See below right.

17c. $1500 = 150A + 40C$

---

14. Give the formulas for finding the circumference and the area of a circle if you know its radius. Tell whether each equation represents a linear relationship.

15. **a.** Write an equation for the distance covered by a car traveling 50 miles per hour for a given number of hours.

   b. Write an equation for the time it takes to go 20 miles at a given rate of speed.

   c. Is either of the equations in parts a and b linear?

Extensions

16. The Small World long-distance phone company charges 55¢ for the first minute of a long-distance call and 23¢ for each additional minute.

   a. How much would a 10-minute long-distance call cost?

   b. If a call costs $4.55, how long did the call last?

   c. Write an equation for the total cost, C, of an m-minute long-distance call.

17. The maximum weight allowed in an elevator is 1500 pounds.

   a. If ten children are in the elevator, how many adults can get in? Assume the average weight per adult is 150 pounds and the average weight per child is 40 pounds.

   b. If six adults are in the elevator, how many children can get in?

   c. Write an equation for the number of adults, A, and the number of children, C, the elevator can hold.

17a.
$$1500 = 150A + 40(10)$$
$$1500 - 400 = 150A + 400 - 400$$
$$1100 = 150A$$
$$\frac{1100}{150} = \frac{150}{150}A$$
$$7.33 = A \text{ (no more than 7 adults)}$$

17b.
$$1500 = 150(6) + 40C$$
$$1500 - 900 = 900 - 900 + 40C$$
$$600 = 40C$$
$$\frac{600}{40} = \frac{40}{40}C$$
$$15 = C \text{ (15 children)}$$

Mathematical Reflections

In this investigation, you learned how to solve equations by operating on the symbols. These questions will help you summarize what you have learned:

1 Describe the symbolic method for solving an equation of the form $y = mx + b$ for the variable x when you know the value of y. Use an example to illustrate the method.

2 Describe how you would use a graphing calculator to solve a linear equation of the form $y = mx + b$ for the variable x when you know the value of y. Use an example to illustrate the process.

Think about your answers to these questions, discuss your ideas with other students and your teacher, and then write a summary of your findings in your journal.

Tips for the Linguistically Diverse Classroom

Diagram Code The Diagram Code technique is described in detail in *Getting to Know Connected Mathematics*. Students use a minimal number of words and drawings, diagrams, or symbols to respond to questions that require writing.
Example: Question 2—A student might answer this question by writing *enter y = 4x + 9* and drawing a graphing calculator screen that shows a *y* range that includes 37 and the words *trace until y = 37*.

TEACHING THE INVESTIGATION

4.1 • Paying in Installments

In this problem, students informally explore methods for finding information about one variable if another variable is known. Students will probably think through the problem and apply some arithmetic. Their methods should provide the catalyst for helping them to develop a more systematic way to think about solving equations. As students will have several opportunities in this unit to solve linear equations symbolically, it will be most useful to them to keep this introduction very informal.

Launch

Pose the problem of buying the CD-ROM drive on an installment plan. Let students solve the problem, in pairs, in any way that makes sense to them. We are not imposing any particular solution method, such as using a table, a graph, or an equation.

Explore

As pairs work, ask questions about their strategies and why they think they make sense. Ask that they write explanations of how they thought about and solved the problem.

When students have the problem under control, assign the follow-up to be done individually and then discussed in pairs. Or, summarize the problem first, then assign the follow-up and discuss it.

Summarize

The summary should build on students' intuition about how to solve the problem of the installment plan. However, unless they are assisted in generalizing their techniques and ideas, they may not be able to make connections between this informal introduction to solving linear equations and the ideas that have been discussed in the unit so far.

Let students share their answers to follow-up question 1. A few will probably have used a table, a graph, or a guess-and-check method, but most will have applied arithmetic reasoning. Take time to explore the connections among these methods. If someone has recorded the entry (0, 30) in a table, connect the information in this pair of values to the equation and the graph. If someone used the process of undoing, or reversing, the operations (see the introduction to Problem 4.2 in the student edition), review their solution with the class to introduce the idea of solving an equation symbolically.

Many students may not see the necessity of reasoning in any way other than arithmetically. One way to be sure students think about alternatives to arithmetic reasoning is to have them work out the problem on a graphing calculator.

> Now that you have a way of thinking about the problem, let's use our graphing calculators to explore the problem in a different way. Enter the equation that represents the store's payment plan, and make a graph of the relationship.

Students will have to think about how to form the equation of the relationship. From this, a discussion of using tables and graphs and reasoning from the equation as ways to solve an equation can proceed naturally.

For the Teacher: Expanding the Installment Problem

Here is how this discussion proceeded in one class. The teacher explained, "We are going to put this on a graphing calculator so that we can look at it the way we looked at the problems in Investigation 3. Remember, we entered the general equations into our calculators."

Students knew they needed an equation for the installment plan in order to use the graphing calculator, and they were able to determine the equation governing the relationship, $C = 30 + 15N$. After they had graphed the equation, the class talked about knowing the y value for total cost ($195) and scanned the table until they found a y value of 195. The teacher pointed out that tables like this would be helpful for salespeople to be able to tell customers how many payments would be needed for a certain purchase.

The teacher then asked, "How could you use a graph to solve this problem?" The class talked about tracing the line until the y value in the display was very close to 195. Then, the teacher posed this question: "What could a salesperson do if a customer wanted to know how many months it would take to pay off a $300 item in installments and the salesperson did not have a graphing calculator?"

The class substituted into the equation they had written to find the value of N, most by using the following procedure:

$300 = 30 + 15N$	*(The customer pays $30 down and owes only $270.)*
$270 = 15N$	*(The customer pays $15 a month—for how many months?)*
$270 \div 15$	*(Find how many $15 payments are needed.)*
$270 \div 15 = 18$	*(It will take 18 months to pay off the item.)*

When you have raised the issues of forming the equation and how it can be used, move on to follow-up question 2. Have several students read the problem they created and its solution. This will give you another chance to help them to describe general solution techniques and to make connections among graphs, tables, arithmetic reasoning, and equations and operations and their inverses. This also gives students experience in talking about equations and their solutions. If the opportunity arises, try to stress solving an equation by "undoing" it.

4.2 • Using the Symbolic Method

In this problem, students are introduced to a method for solving an equation of the form $y = mx + b$ for x if y is given. Undoing, or reversing, the operations is presented informally using the context of the installment-plan problem to guide the reasoning. Students are then challenged to apply the technique.

Launch

Use the summary from Problem 4.1 to introduce the method of solving an equation symbolically. Talk through the strategy of undoing, or reversing, the operations to solve an equation. You may want to use Transparency 4.2A to help you to discuss this strategy as demonstrated in the example in the student edition.

In this discussion, focus on the connections between addition and subtraction, and between multiplication and division. These pairs of operations are the inverses of each other. You can undo addition by subtracting the quantity that you added (and vice versa). You can undo multiplication by dividing by the number that you multiplied by (and vice versa). Many teachers find it useful to demonstrate these ideas using simple whole numbers.

Next, pose the problem of the stove Karen wants to buy on an installment plan. The answer to the problem is not a whole number. You may want to have the class first consider a problem that does have a whole-number answer. For example, change the stove cost to $345. If you pose this problem first, summarize it in a similar manner to the summary below for Problem 4.2.

Have students work in groups of two or three on the problem. Assign the follow-up questions after the summary.

Explore

As groups work, circulate and ask questions to elicit justifications for their approaches to the problem.

> How can you tell what to do first when you are trying to undo the equation to solve for the number of months the customer has to pay?

> How does the equation $305 = 30 + 15x$ relate to the equation $275 = 15x$? Why? What happened to the 30 on the right-hand side of the equation? Why are the two sides still equal?

Summarize

Let students demonstrate their symbolic solution methods at the board. Ask the class to verify each step of the process. Some students will not use a method that keeps the steps in the sequence shown below. You will need to be flexible and look for correct thinking, even if their recording is not as systematic as it could be. The context can help students to make sense of their solution steps.

The equation is $C = 30 + 15N$, where C is the cost of the stove and N is the number of months it will take to pay for the stove at $15 a month.

Thinking	Manipulating the Symbols
The stove costs $305.	$305 = 30 + 15N$
The customer put $30 down on the stove, so $30 can be subtracted from the cost. To keep both sides of the equation equal, 30 must be subtracted from both sides.	$305 - 30 = 30 - 30 - 15N$
There is $275 left to pay, which will be paid off at $15 per month.	$275 = 15N$
The $275 will be paid off over 15 months, or divided by 15. To keep both sides of the equation equal, both sides must be divided by 15.	$\frac{275}{15} = \frac{15}{15}N$
The number of months is $18\frac{1}{3}$.	$18\frac{1}{3} = N$

Notice that each step shows the kind of thinking about undoing the operations that leads to the next step. Students should use the same thinking but will record their work and thoughts in different ways. For example, some students may write the following:

$$305 = 30 + 15N$$
$$305 - 30 = 275$$
$$275 \div 15 = 18\frac{1}{3}$$
$$N = 18\frac{1}{3}$$

Their thinking is correct; their recording is not as formal.

What does $18\frac{1}{3} = N$ mean in this situation? *(Karen has to make payments for 18 months and a third of another month.)*

How will she pay for a third of a month? *(She needs to make a third of a payment, $\frac{1}{3}$ of $15, or $5, in the nineteenth month.)*

Understanding that undoing the operations of an equation is logically equivalent to doing the same operation on both sides of an equation can be explicitly introduced here. You may wish to use Transparency 4.2B to demonstrate the procedure.

In symbols, $30 + 15N = 305$.

In symbols, $30 - 30 + 15N = 305 - 30$ or $15N = 275$.

In symbols, $\frac{15N}{15} = \frac{275}{15}$ or $N = 18\frac{1}{3}$.

To summarize this balancing method, you could present a very simple example. Write $8 = 8$ on the board or overhead.

> What happens if I add the same number—3, for example—to each side of the equality? *(We get 11 on both sides, so we still have a true statement.)*

> What happens if I subtract the same number from both sides?

> What happens if I multiply both sides by the same number, say 2?

> What happens if I divide both sides by the same number, say 2?

> What are your conclusions? *(Adding, subtracting, multiplying, or dividing both sides of an equality by the same thing gives another equality.)*

Help students to see that when they work with equalities, it is important to keep both sides balanced—what is done to one side must be done to the other.

Before the class does the follow-up, put the equation $y = 24x$ on the board. Have the class solve the problem by either balancing the equation or undoing the operations. These two methods are very similar.

For *y* = 24*x*, what is *x* if *y* = 264? How did you find the answer?

Encourage students to discuss solving this symbolically. Because *x* is multiplied by 24, we must divide by 24 to get *x*. It is like finding the number of months it would take to pay for an item on an installment plan if the payments were $24 a month.

Put the equation *y* = 55 + 24*x* on the board.

For *y* = 55 + 24*x*, what is *x* if *y* = 271?

Again, encourage students to think about this symbolically by reversing or undoing the operations. If some students suggest dividing by 24 first, emphasize that then the entire right side must be divided by 24 to give $\frac{55 + 24x}{24}$. This works, but solving the equation will be easier if they undo the addition and subtraction before the multiplication or division.

You may want to show the steps involved in solving the equation this way:

$$\frac{271}{24} = \frac{55 + 24x}{24}$$
$$11\frac{7}{24} = 2\frac{7}{24} + x$$
$$11\frac{7}{24} - 2\frac{7}{24} = 2\frac{7}{24} + x - 2\frac{7}{24}$$
$$9 = x$$

Now have the class do the follow-up, then review the questions. Question 1 will help you check on students' method of solving an equation symbolically. Question 2 is a reminder that there are other ways to solve equations—using a table or a graph, for example. You might demonstrate the use of, or have students use, the graphing calculator to solve one of the equations in question 1.

What are the advantages of each method: using a table, using a graph, and manipulating the symbols in an equation?

As a final wrap-up, pose the following riddle:

I am thinking of a number. If 5 is added to twice my number, the result is 29. What is my number? Describe how you found the answer.

Model students' thinking by writing down the steps. Their thinking may go like this: "Since you added 5 to twice the number, I subtracted 5 from 29 to get 24. This means that 24 is twice your number, so then I divided by 2 to get 12."

Then, model the problem algebraically.

$$29 = 2n + 5$$
$$29 - 5 = 2n + 5 - 5 \qquad \text{Subtract 5 to undo the addition.}$$
$$24 = 2n \qquad \text{Simplify.}$$
$$12 = n \qquad \text{Divide by 2 to undo the multiplication.}$$

4.3 • Analyzing Bones

Students have looked informally at using symbol manipulation to solve equations in context, and they will now use these ideas in new contexts to deepen their understanding. This problem should engage the interest of most students and relate to their science and health classes. The numbers in this problem are measures to the nearest thousandth; calculators should be available to help students do the necessary computation.

Launch

Review the introduction to the forensics information. The problem requires students to choose the appropriate equation and then solve for either the length of a bone or the height of a person. Make sure students understand what each equation means in the context.

> Which equation tells us the relationship between femur length and the height of a female? *(h = 61.412 + 2.317F)*
>
> Which equation could you use to find the length of the humerus of a man who is 200 centimeters tall? *(h = 73.570 + 2.970H)*

Have students work on the problem in groups of two or three. Assign the follow-up to be done individually and then reviewed in groups.

Explore

Some students will have trouble with the decimals in the measures, so be sure calculators are available. Stress that the thinking to solve the equations is the same as that used in the installment-plan problems. You may want to give groups blank transparencies or large sheets of paper on which to record their work for sharing in the summary. You might assign each group a particular part of the problem on which to report.

Encourage students who finish early to try measuring their own bones and height to test how accurate the predictions from the equations are for people their age.

Summarize

Have students share their work for each part of the problem, perhaps having some groups display their solutions. Ask for explanations about why their methods make sense. When sharing their work, students should show each step of their solution and explain their thinking about what makes each step appropriate and valid. Ask other students if what is written and explained is reasonable, and ask whether anyone solved the problem in a different way.

Have several students tell about the equation they graphed in the follow-up and what they think the *x*- and *y*-intercepts mean in this context.

Additional Answers

Answers to Problem 4.2 Follow-Up

1. a. $175 = 2.5x$
     $\frac{175}{2.5} = \frac{2.5}{2.5}x$
     $70 = x$

    b. $64 = 19 + 3x$
     $64 - 19 = 19 - 19 + 3x$
     $45 = 3x$
     $\frac{45}{3} = \frac{3}{3}x$
     $15 = x$

    c. $15 = 2x - 50$
     $15 + 50 = 2x - 50 + 50$
     $65 = 2x$
     $\frac{65}{2} = \frac{2}{2}x$
     $32\frac{1}{2} = x$

    d. $60 = {}^-2x + 14$
     $60 - 14 = {}^-2x + 14 - 14$
     $46 = {}^-2x$
     $\frac{46}{^-2} = \frac{^-2}{^-2}x$
     $^-23 = x$

Answers to Problem 4.3

C. *femur:*
     $152 = 61.412 + 2.317F$
     $90.588 = 2.317F$
     $39.1 = F$ (39.1 cm)

   tibia:
     $152 = 72.572 + 2.533T$
     $79.428 = 2.533T$
     $31.4 = T$ (31.4 cm)

   humerus:
     $152 = 64.977 + 3.144H$
     $87.023 = 3.144H$
     $27.7 = H$ (27.7 cm)

   radius:
     $152 = 73.502 + 3.876R$
     $78.498 = 3.876R$
     $20.3 = R$ (20.3 cm)

D. *femur:*
     $183 = 69.089 + 2.238F$
     $113.911 = 2.238F$
     $50.9 = F$ (50.9 cm)

   tibia:
     $183 = 81.688 + 2.392T$
     $101.312 = 2.392T$
     $42.4 = T$ (42.4 cm)

   humerus:
     $183 = 73.570 + 2.970H$
     $109.43 = 2.970H$
     $36.8 = H$ (36.8 cm)

   radius:
     $183 = 80.405 + 3.650R$
     $102.595 = 3.650R$
     $28.1 = R$ (28.1 cm)

ACE Answers

Applications

10d. The break-even point is when cost equals revenue, which happens at about 151 cakes. Students may look at this on a graph (the *x* value where the lines intersect; see below) or a table.

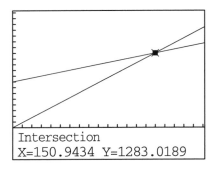

Intersection
X=150.9434 Y=1283.0189

Extensions

16b. m = about 18.4 min (Note: This equation is a little more difficult to solve. Students may reason through it using words, or they may solve it symbolically or with a graphing calculator. Below is the solution done symbolically and using a graphing calculator.)

$$4.55 = 0.55 + 0.23(m - 1)$$
$$4.55 - 0.55 = 0.55 - 0.55 + 0.23(m - 1)$$
$$4 = 0.23(m - 1)$$
$$\frac{4}{0.23} = \frac{0.23}{0.23}(m - 1)$$
$$17.39 = m - 1$$
$$17.39 + 1 = m - 1 + 1$$
$$18.39 = m$$

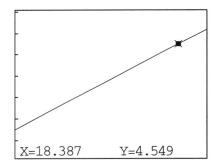

X=18.387   Y=4.549

Exploring Slope

In this investigation, students develop a deeper understanding of linear situations and how to recognize them in different representations. One goal of the investigation is for students to be able to recognize that, in linear situations, there is a constant rate of change between the two variables: for each unit change in x, there is a constant change in y.

In Problem 5.1, Climbing Stairs, students are introduced to the concept of slope through an investigation involving the steepness of a set of stairs. The ratio of rise to run in a set of stairs is a strong visual representation for the ratio of vertical distance to horizontal distance between two points on a line. For any two points on a line, this ratio is a constant. In Problem 5.2, Finding the Slope of a Line, students explore the ratio of vertical change to horizontal change for any pair of points on the graph of a linear equation. This ratio is the slope of the line and it is the coefficient, m, of x in the general equation $y = mx + b$. In Problem 5.3, Connecting Points, students are given two points on a line and are asked to find the slope and the y-intercept. If the y-intercept is not one of the points, students use rates to continue the table to find the point $(0, b)$.

Mathematical and Problem-Solving Goals

- *To develop a more formal understanding of the concept of slope*

- *To find the constant rate, or slope, from a table*

- *To find the slope of a line given two points on the line*

- *To relate the slope and the y-intercept to the equation of a line*

Materials

Problem	For students	For the teacher
All	Graphing calculators, grid paper (provided as blackline masters)	Transparencies 5.1 to 5.3 (optional), transparent grids (optional; copy the blackline masters onto transparency film), overhead display model of students' graphing calculator (optional)
5.1	Set of stairs to measure, tape measures (preferably metric), string	
5.3	Blank transparencies (optional)	

Student Pages 64–79 | **Teaching the Investigation 79a–79m**

5.1

Climbing Stairs

Launch

- A day or two prior to the problem, talk about the steepness of stairs and ask students to investigate stairs at home and school.

- Talk about students' findings, and how steepness might be indicated mathematically.

Explore

- Have each group measure a set of stairs and determine the ratio of rise to run.

- Remind groups to measure at least two different steps and to organize their findings.

Summarize

- As a class, review the groups' findings about the various sets of stairs.

- Have groups work on the follow-up, then review the answers and drawings.

- Discuss the definition of *slope*.

Assignment Choices

ACE questions 1–4, 26, 28, 29, and unassigned choices from earlier problems

---

Exploring Slope

All the linear situations you have explored in this unit involve rates. For example, you worked with walking rates expressed as meters per second and pledge rates expressed as dollars per mile. In these situations, you found that the rate affects the following things:

- the steepness of the graph
- the coefficient, *m*, of *x* in the equation $y = mx + b$
- the amount the *y* values in the table change for each unit change in the *x* values

All of these things are related to the *slope* of the line. In this investigation, you will learn what the slope of a line is, and you will discover how you can determine the slope from the graph, equation, or table of values for a linear relationship.

5.1 Climbing Stairs

Climbing stairs is good exercise. Some athletes run up and down stairs as part of their training. The steepness of stairs determines how difficult they are to climb. Stairs that are very steep are more difficult to climb than stairs that rise gradually. Examining the steepness of stairs can help you understand the idea of steepness, or slope, of a line.

Think about this!

Consider the following questions about the stairs you encounter at home, in your school, and in other buildings:

- How can you describe the steepness of the stairs?

- Is the steepness the same between any two consecutive steps for a particular set of stairs?

The steepness of stairs is determined by the ratio of the **rise** to the **run** for each step. The rise and run are labeled in the diagram below.

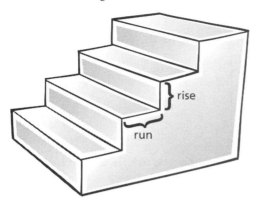

Carpenters have developed guidelines to ensure the stairs they build are relatively easy for a person to climb. In some states, carpenters work with these guidelines:

- The ratio of rise to run for each step should be between 0.45 and 0.60.
- The rise plus the run for each step should be between 17 and 17.5 inches.

Problem 5.1

Determine the steepness of a set of stairs.

To calculate the steepness you will need to measure the rise and the run of a step. Measure at least two steps in the set of stairs you choose. Make a sketch of the stairs, and label it with the measurements you found.

How do the stairs you measured compare with the guidelines above?

Answers to Problem 5.1

Answers will vary.

Finding the Slope of a Line

At a Glance

Grouping: individuals, then small groups

Launch

■ Discuss the definition of *slope*.

■ As a class, look for patterns in the table for equation i and relate the table and the graph to the slope.

■ Make the connection between horizontal and vertical change and the slope.

Explore

■ Have individuals work on the other four equations and share findings in groups.

■ As students work, ask questions about the slope between specific points.

Summarize

■ Ask students to share the slope they found for each line.

■ Discuss the concept of the slope in detail, trying to help students understand that the slope is the same between any two points on a line.

Assignment Choices

ACE questions 5–9, 18–20, 24, 25, 32, 33, and unassigned choices from earlier problems

---

■ **Problem 5.1 Follow-Up**

1. Make and label a scale drawing of stairs that don't meet the carpenters' guidelines. Explain why the stairs you drew are steeper (or less steep) than the stairs described in the guidelines.

2. You can use the ideas about the steepness of stairs to find the steepness of a ramp.

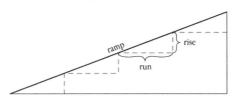

In one state, the construction code for an access ramp is a rise of 1 foot for a run of 12 feet. The access ramp at a football stadium in this state has a rise of 1 foot for a run of 8 feet. Many people in wheelchairs cannot get their chairs up the ramp without help. Make scale drawings of the stadium ramp and a ramp meeting the state code.

5.2 **Finding the Slope of a Line**

The method for finding the steepness of stairs suggests a way to find the steepness of a line. A line drawn from the bottom step to the top step of a set of stairs will touch each step in one point. The rise and the run of a step are the vertical and the horizontal changes, respectively, between two points on the line.

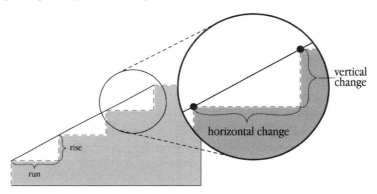

Answers to Problem 5.1 Follow-Up

1. Possible answer: These stairs are too steep ($\frac{8}{12}$ = 0.67) to meet the guidelines; the maximum ratio of rise to run is 0.60.

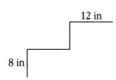

2. This problem requires students to find a pictorial way to represent the two access ramps. They will have to interpret the given ratios in their model. Possible drawing:

If you choose two points on a line, you can draw a "step" from one point to the other.

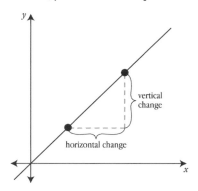

The steepness of the line is the ratio of rise to run, or vertical change to horizontal change, for this step. We call the steepness of a line its **slope.**

$$\text{slope} = \frac{\text{vertical change}}{\text{horizontal change}}$$

Unlike the steepness of stairs, the slope of a line can be negative. To determine the slope of a line, you need to consider the direction, or sign, of the vertical and horizontal change from one point to another. If one of these changes is negative, the slope will be negative. Lines that slant *upward* from left to right have *positive slope;* lines that slant *downward* from left to right have *negative slope.*

Line with Positive Slope

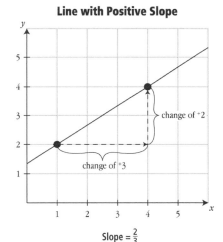

Slope = $\frac{2}{3}$

Line with Negative Slope

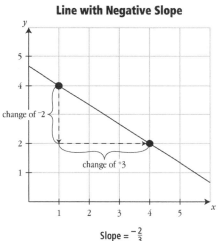

Slope = $-\frac{2}{3}$

Connecting Points

At a Glance

Grouping:
pairs

Launch

- Talk with the class about how the slope and the *y*-intercept of a line might be found from two points on the line.

Explore

- As you circulate, ask questions about how students are finding the slope and the *y*-intercept of each line.

- Have students move on to the follow-up, or assign it after the summary of the problem.

Summarize

- Have students share their answers to the problem, and talk about how to find the slope of a line given a graph, a table, or an equation.

- Have students work on the follow-up if they haven't already, and discuss their answers.

Assignment Choices

ACE questions 10–17, 21–23, 27, 30, 31, and unassigned choices from earlier problems

Assessment

It is appropriate to use Quiz B after this problem.

Problem 5.2

Do parts A–D for each equation below.

i. $y = 2x$ **ii.** $y = {}^-3x$ **iii.** $y = 5 + 2x$
iv. $y = \frac{1}{2}x + 2$ **v.** $y = 2 - 3x$

A. Make a table of *x* and *y* values for the equation. Use the *x* values ⁻3, ⁻2, ⁻1, 0, 1, 2, 3, and 4.

B. On grid paper, make a graph of the equation.

C. Choose two points on the line, and compute the ratio of the vertical change to the horizontal change from one point to the other. Would you get the same ratio if you had chosen two different points? Choose two different points, and check your answer.

D. The ratio you computed in part C is the slope of the line. How is the slope of the line related to the table of values for the line? How is it related to the equation for the line?

■ **Problem 5.2 Follow-Up**

Use the ideas you have learned about slope and about vertical and horizontal change to explain why the line for $y = 3x$ is steeper than the line for $y = x$.

5.3 **Connecting Points**

For any two points, there is exactly one straight line that can be drawn through both points. In this problem, you will be given the coordinates of two points. Your task will be to find information about the line through these points—including its slope, its *y*-intercept, and the coordinates of other points that lie on the line.

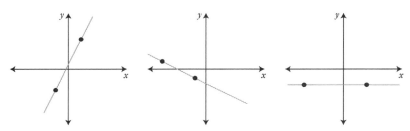

Answers to Problem 5.2

See page 79k.

Answer to Problem 5.2 Follow-Up

The line $y = 3x$ is steeper than $y = x$ because $y = 3x$ means that for every 1 step (or unit) you take horizontally, you take 3 steps (or units) of change vertically; in $y = x$, every 1 step of horizontal change is associated with only 1 step of vertical change. The greater vertical change for the same horizontal change makes the line steeper.

Problem 5.3

Do parts A–E for each pair of points below.

i. (2, 6) and (0, 4)	**ii.** (2, 3) and (4, 6)	**iii.** (0, 3) and (1, 4)
iv. (⁻1, 3) and (1, 0)	**v.** (1, 4) and (3, 4)	**vi.** (4, 1) and (⁻4, 2)

A. Plot the points on a coordinate grid, and draw the line that passes through them.

B. Do the *y* values for points on the line increase, decrease, or stay the same as the *x* values increase?

C. Find the slope of the line.

D. Mark and label at least three other points on the line, and record the *x* and *y* values for the points in an organized table. Does the pattern in your table confirm the slope you found in part B?

E. Use the graph or the table to find the *y*-intercept of the line.

■ **Problem 5.3 Follow-Up**

1. How can you use the slope of a line to determine whether the line slants upward from left to right, slants downward from left to right, or is horizontal?

2. The table below represents a linear relationship. Copy the table, and use the pattern to fill in the missing entries. Find the slope and the *y*-intercept of the graph of this relationship. Explain how you found your answers.

x	?	⁻6	⁻5	⁻4	⁻3	⁻2	⁻1	?	?
y	?	⁻10	⁻7	⁻4	⁻1	2	5	?	?

3. Confirm that the table below represents a linear relationship. What is the slope of the graph of this relationship?

x	46	47.1	48.1	49	50.1
y	31.5	34.14	36.54	38.7	41.34

Answers to Problem 5.3

See page 79l.

Answers to Problem 5.3 Follow-Up

1. If the slope is positive, the line slopes upward; if the slope is negative, the line slopes downward; and if the slope is 0, the line is horizontal.

2. The slope is $\frac{3}{1}$ because the *y* value increases by 3 for every increase of 1 in the *x* value. The *y*-intercept is the point where *x* = 0, or (0, 8).

x	**⁻7**	⁻6	⁻5	⁻4	⁻3	⁻2	⁻1	0	1
y	**⁻13**	⁻10	⁻7	⁻4	⁻1	2	5	8	11

3. See page 79m.

Answers

Applications

1. slope = 3,
y-intercept = 10

2. slope = 0.5,
y-intercept = 0

3. slope = ⁻3,
y-intercept = 0

4. slope = ⁻5,
y-intercept = 2

5. slope = 2,
y-intercept = 0,
$y = 2x$

6. slope = 1,
y-intercept = 3.5,
$y = x + 3.5$

7. slope = 2,
y-intercept = ⁻1,
$y = 2x - 1$

8. slope = ⁻2,
y-intercept = 5,
$y = 5 - 2x$

9. slope = ⁻3,
y-intercept = ⁻2,
$y = ⁻3x - 2$

As you work on these ACE questions, use your calculator whenever you need it.

Applications

In 1–4, find the slope and the y-intercept of the line represented by the equation.

1. $y = 10 + 3x$ **2.** $y = 0.5x$

3. $y = ⁻3x$ **4.** $y = ⁻5x + 2$

In 5–9, the table represents a linear relationship.

- Give the slope and the y-intercept of the graph of the relationship.
- Determine which of the following equations fits the relationship:

$$y = 5 - 2x \quad y = 2x \quad y = ⁻3x - 2 \quad y = 2x - 1 \quad y = x + 3.5$$

5.

x	0	1	2	3	4
y	0	2	4	6	8

6.

x	0	1	2	3	4
y	3.5	4.5	5.5	6.5	7.5

7.

x	0	1	2	3	4
y	⁻1	1	3	5	7

8.

x	0	1	2	3	4
y	5	3	1	⁻1	⁻3

9.

x	1	2	3	4	5
y	⁻5	⁻8	⁻11	⁻14	⁻17

In 10–13, find the slope of the line, and write an equation for the line.

10.

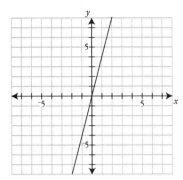

11.

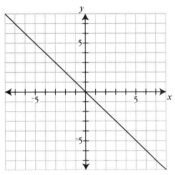

12.

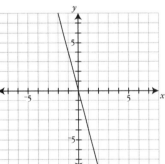

10. slope = 4, $y = 4x$

11. slope = $^-1$, $y = ^-x$

12. slope = $^-4$, $y = ^-4x$

13. slope = ⁻0.5, y = ⁻0.5x

14a. See below right.

14b. slope = 1

14c. y-intercept = 0

14d. y = x

15a. See below right.

15b. slope = ⁻1

15c. y-intercept = 0

15d. y = ⁻x

16a. See below right.

16b. slope = ⁻1

16c. y-intercept = ⁻5

16d. y = ⁻x − 5

17a. See below right.

17b. slope = 0

17c. y-intercept = 6

17d. y = 6

18a.

x	y
⁻4	⁻4
0	0
4	4

18b. See page 79m.

18c. slope = 1

19a.

x	y
⁻2	⁻6
0	⁻2
2	2

19b. See page 79m.

19c. slope = 2

20a.

x	y
⁻4	4
0	2
4	0

20b. See page 79m.

20c. slope = ⁻0.5

21. b, e, and i

22. a, f, and j

23. c, d, g, and h

13.

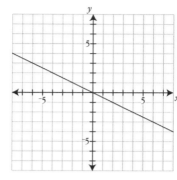

In 14–17, do parts a–d.

14. (0, 0) and (3, 3) **15.** (⁻1, 1) and (3, ⁻3)

16. (0, ⁻5) and (⁻2, ⁻3) **17.** (3, 6) and (5, 6)

    a. Plot the points on a coordinate grid, and draw a line through them.

    b. Find the slope of the line.

    c. Estimate the y-intercept from the graph.

    d. Use your answers from parts b and c to write an equation for the line.

In 18–20, do parts a–c.

18. y = x **19.** y = 2x + ⁻2 **20.** y = ⁻0.5x + 2

    a. Make a table of x and y values for the equation.

    b. Make a graph of the equation.

    c. Find the slope of the graph.

In 21–23, determine which linear relationships in a–j fit the description.

21. The line for this relationship has positive slope.

22. The line for this relationship has a slope of ⁻2.

23. The line for this relationship has a slope of 0.

14a.

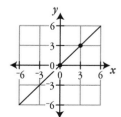

15a.

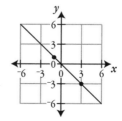

16a.

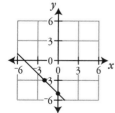

17a.

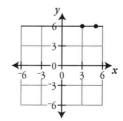

a.

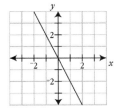

b.

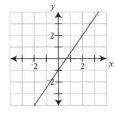

c.

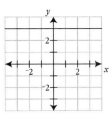

d.

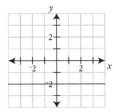

e.

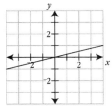

f.

x	⁻3	⁻2	⁻1	0
y	7	5	3	1

g.

x	⁻4	⁻2	⁻1	0
y	2	2	2	2

h. $y = 1.5$ **i.** $y = {}^-5 + 3x$ **j.** $y = 4 + {}^-2x$

24. a. Find the slope of the line represented by the equation $y = x - 1$.

    b. Make a table of x and y values for the equation $y = x - 1$. How is the slope related to the table entries?

24a. slope = 1

24b. The slope is the change in the y values compared to the change in the x values between two points in the table.

x	y
⁻2	⁻3
⁻1	⁻2
0	⁻1
1	0
2	1

25a. slope = ⁻2

25b. The slope is the change in the *y* values for a change of 1 unit in the *x* values between two points in the table.

x	*y*
⁻2	7
⁻1	5
0	3
1	1
2	⁻1

26a. $T = 12 - 3n$

26b. *y*-intercept = 12; The *y*-intercept gives the starting temperature after 0 hours.

26c. slope = ⁻3; The slope tells the rate of change (decrease) in temperature for each hour.

27a. $m = 0.50n$

27b. slope = 0.50

Connections

28. See below right.

---

25. **a.** Find the slope of the line represented by the equation $y = ⁻2x + 3$.

  b. Make a table of *x* and *y* values for the equation $y = ⁻2x + 3$. How is the slope related to the table entries?

26. At noon, the temperature was 12°F. For the next 24 hours, the temperature fell by an average of 3°F an hour.

  a. Write an equation for the temperature, *T*, *n* hours after noon.

  b. What is the *y*-intercept of the line the equation represents? What does the *y*-intercept tell you about this situation?

  c. What is the slope of the line the equation represents? What does the slope tell you about this situation?

27. Natasha never manages to make her allowance last for a whole week, so she borrows money from her sister. Suppose Natasha borrows 50 cents every week.

  a. Write an equation for the amount of money, *m*, Natasha owes her sister after *n* weeks.

  b. What is the slope of the graph of the equation from part a?

Connections

28. In Europe, many hills have signs indicating their steepness, or slope. Here are some examples:

 This means for each 4 meters in run the hill rises by 1 meter.

 This means for each 15 meters in run the hill falls by 1 meter.

On a coordinate grid, sketch hills with the above slopes.

28. $y = \frac{1}{4}x$

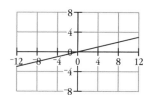

$y = ⁻\frac{1}{15}x$

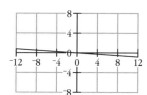

29. In 1980, the town of Rio Rancho, located on a mesa outside Santa Fe, New Mexico, was destined for obscurity. But as a result of hard work by its city officials, it began adding manufacturing jobs at a fast rate. As a result, the city's population grew 239% from 1980 to 1990, making Rio Rancho the fastest-growing "small city" in the United States. The population of Rio Rancho in 1990 was 37,000.

    a. What was the population of Rio Rancho in 1980?

    b. If the same rate of population increase continues, what will the population be in the year 2000?

30. James and Janna share a veterinary practice. They each make farm visits two days a week. They take cellular phones on these trips to keep in touch with the office. James makes his farm visits on weekdays. His cellular phone rate is $14.95 a month plus $0.50 a minute. Janna makes her visits on Saturday and Sunday and is charged a weekend rate of $29.95 a month plus $0.25 a minute.

    a. Write an equation for each billing plan.

    b. Is it possible for James' cellular phone bill to be more than Janna's? Explain how you know this.

    c. Is it possible for James' and Janna's phone bills to be for the same amount? How many minutes of phone calls would each person have to make for their bills to be equal?

    d. Janna finds another phone company that offers one rate for both weekday and weekend calls. The billing plan for this company can be expressed by the equation $A = 25 + 0.25m$, where A is the total monthly bill and m is the number of minutes of calls. Compare this billing plan with the other two plans.

29a. $2.39P + P = 37,000$, so $P = 10,914.45428$ or approximately 10,914 people in 1980

29b. $P = 2.39(37,000) + 37,000 = 125,430$ people in 2000

30a. $A_{James} = 14.95 + 0.50m$; $A_{Janna} = 29.95 + 0.25m$

30b. yes; Thinking of the graphs makes it clear that James' phone bill will be lower for a number of minutes close to 0. For example, for 0 minutes (the y-intercept) James' bill is $14.95 and Janna's is $29.95. James' bill will eventually be higher than Janna's because the rate, or slope, is greater.

30c. See below left.

30d. This plan will cost less than James' plan if the time charged is more than 40 minutes. It will always cost less than Janna's plan because the y-intercept is lower and the rate, or slope, is the same.

30c. yes; They will be the same when $A_{James} = A_{Janna}$. This happens at 60 minutes of calls. (Note: Students can do this problem on the graphing calculator by making a table or graph, or using a paper-and-pencil method.)

X	Y₁	Y₂
10	19.95	32.45
20	24.95	34.95
30	29.95	37.45
40	34.95	39.95
50	39.95	42.45
60	44.95	44.95
70	49.95	47.45
X = 60		

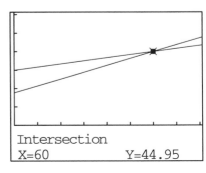

Intersection
X=60   Y=44.95

Extensions

31a. i. slope = 10,
$y = 10x$
ii. slope = 10, $y = 10x$
iii. slope = 10, $y = 10x$

Extensions

31. **a.** Find the slope of each line below, and write an equation for the line.

i.

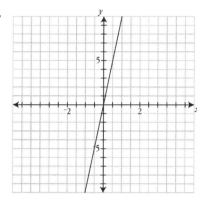

ii.

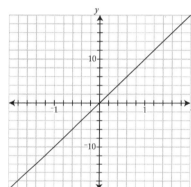

iii.

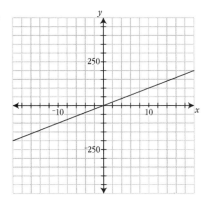

b. Compare the slopes of the three lines.

c. How are the three graphs similar? How are they different?

32. On a flight from Boston to Detroit last March, passengers were able to watch a monitor that gave the altitude and the outside temperature. Two middle school teachers on the flight decided to try to figure out a formula for the temperature, t, in degrees Fahrenheit at an altitude of a feet above sea level. One teacher said the formula is $t = 46 - 0.003a$, and the other said it is $t = 46 + 0.003a$.

a. Which formula makes more sense to you? Why?

b. The Detroit Metropolitan Airport is 620 feet above sea level. Use the formula you chose in part a to find the temperature at the airport.

c. Does the temperature you found in part b seem reasonable? Why or why not?

31b. The slopes of the three lines are the same.

31c. The three graphs have the same slope and the same equation. The scales on the axes are different, which makes the graphs look different.

32a. Temperature should decrease as altitude increases, so $t = 46 - 0.003a$ makes more sense.

32b. $t = 46 - 0.003(620) = 44.14°F$

32c. A temperature of 44°F makes sense for Detroit in March.

33a. Before liftoff, the spaceship is stationary (it is on the launchpad awaiting ignition). At time = 0 the engines are ignited. It takes almost four seconds for the huge spaceship to move, but its altitude increases rapidly thereafter.

33b. Before liftoff, the slope is 0. The rate of increase in altitude during this time (while the spaceship is stationary) is 0.

33. The graph below shows the altitude of a spaceship from 10 seconds before liftoff through 7 seconds after liftoff.

a. Describe the relationship between the altitude of the spaceship and time.

b. What is the slope for the part of the graph that is a straight line? What does this slope represent in this situation?

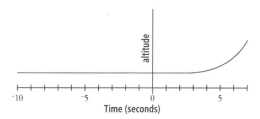

Mathematical Reflections

In this investigation, you learned about the slope, or steepness, of a line, and you discovered how to determine the slope from a table, a graph, or an equation. These questions will help you summarize what you have learned:

1 Explain what the slope of a line is.

2 How can you find the slope of a line from its equation? From its graph? From a table of values for the line? From the coordinates of two points on the line?

3 Describe how information about y-intercept and slope allows you to compare two equations. For example, how can you decide which equation has a steeper graph? How can you can you determine where the graphs of the equations cross the y-axis?

4 In *Comparing and Scaling*, you used ratios to make comparisons. What similarities are there between the way you used ratios in *Comparing and Scaling* and the way you have used slope in this unit?

Think about your answers to these questions, discuss your ideas with other students and your teacher, and then write a summary of your findings in your journal.

Possible Answers

1. The slope describes the steepness of a line. It is the ratio of vertical change to horizontal change. If it is positive, the line is increasing from left to right; if it is negative, the line is decreasing from left to right. If the slope is 0, the line is horizontal. This is like walking on a flat surface as opposed to up or down a hill.

2. If the equation of a line is in the form $y = mx + b$, then m is the slope. In a table for a linear relationship, the slope can be found by finding the change in two x values and the change in two corresponding y values. The slope is the ratio of the change in the y values to the change in the x values. In a graph, find two points on the graph and then find the difference between the y-coordinates (or the vertical change) and the difference between the x-coordinates (or the horizontal change) and then find the ratio of vertical change to horizontal change.

3. See page 79m.

4. See page 79m.

Tips for the Linguistically Diverse Classroom

Diagram Code The Diagram Code technique is described in detail in *Getting to Know Connected Mathematics*. Students use a minimal number of words and drawings, diagrams, or symbols to respond to questions that require writing. Example: Question 1—A student might answer this question by drawing stairs and marking the slope as the ratio of the vertical change to the horizontal change. The student could also show three lines: a line increasing from left to right labeled with a + sign, a line decreasing from left to right labeled with a – sign, and a horizontal line labeled *slope = 0.*

TEACHING THE INVESTIGATION

5.1 • Climbing Stairs

In this problem students investigate the ratio of the vertical rise to the horizontal run between two steps in a set of stairs. They then compare the rise and run of a set of stairs to the vertical and horizontal change between any two points on a line. Prior to having students work on the problem, you may want to locate sets of stairs that your class can measure.

Launch

Introduce the context of this problem a day or so before you intend to have the class work on it. This will allow students time for some experimentation. Discuss the fact that stair climbing is a popular aerobic exercise.

> Does the steepness of a set of stairs affect the exercise?

Tell the class that, for homework, they are to examine the stairs in their house, apartment, or school. Ask them to look for several sets of stairs with steps of various sizes. Climbing different sets of stairs will allow students to "experience" steepness. Challenge them to think about what makes one set of steps feel steeper than another.

> Do all stairs have the same steepness?

> How can we determine the steepness of a set of stairs?

> How could you use a mathematical measure to give an indication of steepness?

Ask students to take measurements of at least two different sets of steps that they think might help in indicating steepness.

When you are ready to launch the problem, ask for suggestions about what factors seem to influence the steepness of a set of stairs.

> What measures might give us a mathematical way to compare steepness?

If no one mentions the rise and the run, suggest these as possible measures. Draw a picture of a set of stairs and indicate the rise and the run. Go over the carpenters' guidelines in the student edition now, or wait until after students have collected their data and then have them compare their ratios to the guidelines. Save the follow-up questions for the summary.

For the Teacher: A Ratio for Steepness

In this problem, a set of stairs is used as a physical model for slope. If a line (or piece of string) is drawn from the top step to the bottom step, the steps represent the vertical and horizontal change between two points on the line. By comparing the ratio of the vertical change to the horizontal change between any two steps, students will discover that the ratio is constant. This ratio is the slope of the line or the rate of change in a linear situation.

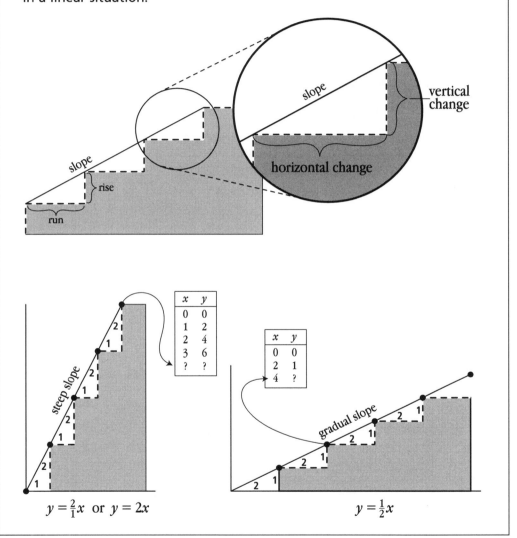

Have students work in groups of three or four to measure the rise and the run of a set of stairs and then compute the ratio of the rise to the run.

Explore

Assign a different set of stairs to each group if possible. Remind groups that they need to measure more than one step in each set of stairs and to compare the ratios with the carpenters' guidelines.

When groups have recorded their measures, have them organize their findings about the ratio of rise to run between several of the steps in the staircase. Also have them look at the ratios of the rise to the run on the staircases they measured for homework.

Summarize

Let each group report on the stairs they investigated. Make a class record of the stairs and measures that are reported. Compare the ratios for various sets of stairs.

> Which is the steepest set of stairs in our list? Which is the least steep? How do you know?
>
> Do the steps within a set of stairs all have the same steepness, or do they differ? How do you know?
>
> Can you order the entire list of stairs from least to greatest in terms of steepness?

These questions focus attention on using the ratio to characterize steepness in a mathematical sense. Steer the discussion to measures of rise and run. Make the connection to the *Comparing and Scaling* unit, in which students formed ratios as a way to make comparisons.

Talk about why stairs are different in different situations. For instance, when space is limited, stairs may be made steeper to minimize the space they require. In buildings built before building codes, stairs may vary a great deal. In buildings in which people who may have trouble walking will be, stairs may be much less steep than usual.

If you have not done so already, talk about the carpenters' guidelines given in the student edition. Ask questions about how students' measurements relate to the guidelines.

How do the ratios of the stairs we measured compare to the carpenters' guidelines? Which meet the standards? Which do not?

What do you think influences a builder's decision about the run of a set of steps? What do you think influences a builder's decision about the rise of a set of steps?

In answering these questions, students should be making comparisons using the ratio of the rise to run, which leads into the topic of the first follow-up question. Before doing the follow-up, you could offer the following challenge:

Let's think about another common object that you have climbed: a ladder. How can you use what you have learned so far to help make sense of steepness as it applies to ladders? What would make a ladder feel steep? What would make the same ladder feel less steep?

The angle of the ladder against the building will affect the ratio of the rise to the run and hence affect how it feels to climb the ladder.

Read the follow-up with the class. Give students time to draw models for a set of stairs, the football stadium ramp, and a ramp that fits the code.

Use this summary to informally define slope and to lead into the launch of the next problem. An illustration of stairs will help you define slope, as it will help students to make visual connections between things they have physically experienced and the lines on a graph representing linear relationships.

5.2 • Finding the Slope of a Line

In this problem students formalize the concept of slope as the ratio of vertical change to horizontal change between any two points on a line.

Launch

Use the summary from the last problem and the presentation in the student edition to present a formal definition of slope.

Slope is the ratio of the vertical change to the horizontal change between two points on a line, or

$$\text{slope} = \frac{\text{vertical change}}{\text{horizontal change}}$$

You might draw a picture to demonstrate this idea.

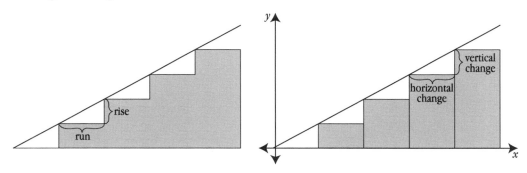

Do not give students the definition of change in y- and x-coordinates at this time $\left(\frac{y_2 - y_1}{x_2 - x_1}\right)$. It is important that they have a visual image of the vertical and horizontal change between two points before trying to understand the symbolic generalization.

Continue the discussion by asking these questions:

> How does the ratio of rise to run affect the steepness of a set of stairs?
>
> How do you think the ratio of rise to run will affect the steepness of a line?

Using the first equation in the problem, $y = 2x$, review how to generate a table and a graph from an equation on a graphing calculator (if students' calculators cannot generate tables, ask them to make a table by hand).

> What patterns do you see in the table?

If students cannot see any patterns, be more specific.

> As x increases by 1 unit, how much does y increase? *(by 2 units)* How is this change represented in the table? *(The table shows a change of 1 unit between x values and a corresponding change of 2 units between y values.)* How is it represented on the graph? *(If you move from a point on the line to the right 1 unit and up 2 units, you will be at another point on the line.)*

Help students to see the connection between the changes in the table and the vertical and horizontal change between two points on the graph.

> What is the ratio of the vertical change to the horizontal change? *($\frac{2}{1}$)*
>
> What happens to the ratio of vertical to horizontal change if it is measured between two points that are farther apart on the line, such as ($^-2$, $^-4$) and (1, 2)? *(The ratio between these two points is $\frac{6}{3}$, which is equivalent to $\frac{2}{1}$; the ratio remains the same.)*

This is an important point that will need to be discussed on several occasions: *The ratio between any horizontal change and its corresponding vertical change is constant for a given linear relationship.*

Demonstrate that this ratio is the same no matter what two points are chosen. For example, for the points (0, 0) and (1, 2), the ratio is $\frac{2}{1}$ or 2. For the points (3, 6) and (5, 10), the ratio is $\frac{4}{2}$ or $\frac{2}{1}$ or 2. Draw a picture to help students find the vertical and horizontal change.

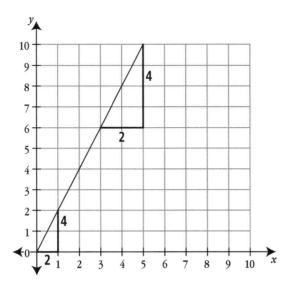

What is the slope of this line?

Make sure students understand the description of positive slope and negative slope that is given on page 67 of the student edition.

Explore

Let students work on the remaining four equations individually and then share their work in groups to be sure everyone in the group is making sense of the problem. Have students look at the follow-up, which asks them to use the ideas in the problem to explain why one line is steeper than another.

As you circulate, ask questions about the slope between specific pairs of points on the lines that students are exploring. Choose points that are 1 unit apart on the x-axis as well as points that are more than 1 unit apart. For example, if a student is working on equation iii, $y = 5 + 2x$, ask:

Start at the point on the graph where x is 3. What is the corresponding value of y? Now look at the point on the graph where x is 5. What is the corresponding value of y? What is the horizontal change and the vertical change between these two points? How do you know?

What does this tell you about the slope of the line representing the equation? *(The ratio of the vertical change to the horizontal change is the slope of the line.)*

If you looked at the ratio of the vertical change to the horizontal change between two other points on the line, what would the ratio be? How do you know?

Summarize

Have students share the slope (the ratio of vertical change to horizontal change) they found for each line they graphed. Ask questions to assess their understanding of the concept of the slope of a line.

How is the slope of a line related to the table of values for the line? *(The slope is the same as the ratio of change between two values of y compared to the change between the corresponding values of x.)*

How can you find the slope of a line using the related table of values? *(You write the amount of change between two y values and the amount of change between the corresponding x values as a ratio. This ratio is the slope.)*

Using the table, how can you decide whether the slope, or ratio, is positive or negative? By looking at the table, how can you tell whether the graph of the points will produce a line with a positive slope (and slant upward from right to left) or a negative slope (and slant downward from right to left)? *(If the y values increase as the x values increase, the line will slant upward and have a positive slope. If the y values decrease as the x values increase, the line will slant downward and have a negative slope.)*

How can you find the slope of a line using the equation? *(The coefficient of x in the equation is the same as the ratio of vertical change to horizontal change.)*

How can you find the slope of a line using the graph?

For the Teacher: Another Slope Graphic

Two vertical number lines can be used as another representation of the change in *y* related to the change in *x*. Some students find a drawing like this one helpful. It shows that as *x* is changing in a regular way, *y* is also changing in a regular way—even though the two changes may be different. A change of 1 unit in *x* is accompanied by a change of 2 units in *y*.

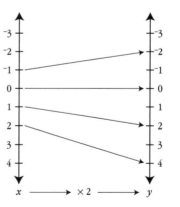

An important observation to help students make is that *no matter what two points on a line are chosen, the ratio of the vertical change to the horizontal change is always the same.*

For the Teacher: Slope and Similar Triangles

Notice that the line itself and the horizontal line drawn through the *y*-intercept form an angle. Three vertical segments are then drawn to the horizontal line, forming three similar triangles. The ratio of the vertical to the horizontal leg is the same for all similar triangles, so the slopes must be the same.

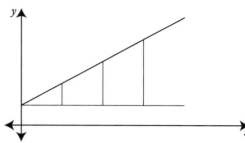

The vertical change to the horizontal change is always the same between any two points on a line.

In later math courses, students will encounter another name for this ratio: it is the *tangent* of the angle formed by the line of the equation and the *x*-axis. The angle is called the *angle of inclination.*

If you know one point on the graph of a line and you know the slope of the line, how can you use the slope to create a set of points that all lie on the line?

For example, if the slope $\frac{2}{1}$ and the point (1, 2) are known, the points (2, ?), (3, ?), and (0, ?) can be found using the slope by "walking" 1 unit to the right and 2 units up on the graph:

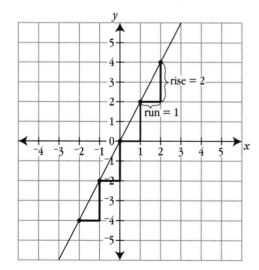

The topics covered in this summary will lead into the launch of the next problem.

5.3 • Connecting Points

In this problem, students apply their knowledge of linear relationships. They are given the coordinates of two points and are asked to find the slope of the line, the y-intercept, and other points that lie on the line. They can use the graph or apply the concept of rate, or slope, to generate table entries until they reach the point $(0, b)$. (Once the slope, m, and y-intercept, b, are known, students can find the equation of the line in the form $y = mx + b$; however, they are not asked to do that in this problem. Writing the equation for a line given two points is the focus of Problem 6.1.)

Launch

Use the summary of the last problem to lead into the launch of this problem.

> If you are given two points, you could draw a line connecting them. Could there be more than one line through two given points? Why or why not?

Student will intuitively recognize that there can be only one line through two points (you may need to clarify the distinction between a *line segment* and a *line;* the line that stretches infinitely in both directions is unique).

> If you draw a line through two points, what kind of relationship does that represent? *(a linear relationship)* If we know two points that are on that line, how can we find the slope of the line? For example, if we know the points (2, 6) and (0, 4), how can we find the slope of the line that goes through them?

Sketch a graph of the line, and let students describe how to find its slope. They might talk about how there is a change of positive 2 in the vertical direction for a change of positive 2 in the horizontal direction. This gives a slope of $\frac{2}{2}$, or 1.

> What is the y-intercept of the line that passes through these two points? *(Since we know the point (0, 4), we know that the y-intercept is 4.)*

The intent of this problem is to help students connect the information they have about linear relationships with finding the slope of a line given two points on that line. Students have information about the graph of a linear relationship; the question is how to use that information to find the slope and, eventually, the y-intercept. If your students had difficulty working through the example above, a picture might help them to visualize the vertical and horizontal changes.

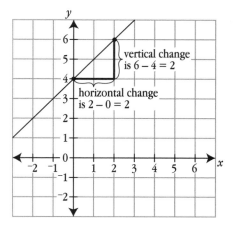

If necessary, work through another example with the class, perhaps an example in which one of the two points is *not* the *y*-intercept.

When they are ready, let students work in pairs on the problem.

Explore

As you circulate, ask questions that encourage students to explain how to find the slope and the *y*-intercept of a line given two points on the line. If a student is having trouble, have him or her work through an example with you present to ask questions. You will be able to see what is causing the student difficulty and help to sort it out.

If students are making sense of the ideas in the problem, have them continue working and do the follow-up questions with their partner. If they are struggling, have the class do the follow-up after you have summarized Problem 5.3 as a class.

For students who finish early, you might ask them to redo their graphs from part A on transparencies for sharing in the summary.

Summarize

Have students share their answers and discuss how they found them. Help them to connect negative, positive, or zero slope with decreasing, increasing, or horizontal lines. Emphasize that when we visually scan a graph from left to right, we are observing what happens to the *y* values as the *x* values increase.

Summarize the discussion and the ideas of the unit by talking with the class about methods for finding the slope given an equation, a table, or a graph (or two points on a line).

Ask how students found the *y*-intercept when given only two pairs of points on the line. If they talk about graphing the two points, drawing a line through them, and reading where the line crosses the *y*-axis, ask if there is ever a problem with that method. Help them to realize that although this is a reasonable way of finding the *y*-intercept, depending on the scaling of the graph and the linear relationship, it might give them only an approximation.

If students have already done the follow-up questions, have them discuss their findings. If not, assign them now and then have them share their answers.

Additional Answers

Answers to Problem 5.2

A.

i.

x	y
-3	-6
-2	-4
-1	-2
0	0
1	2
2	4
3	6
4	8

ii.

x	y
-3	9
-2	6
-1	3
0	0
1	-3
2	-6
3	-9
4	-12

iii.

x	y
-3	-1
-2	1
-1	3
0	5
1	7
2	9
3	11
4	13

iv.

x	y
-3	$\frac{1}{2}$
-2	1
-1	$1\frac{1}{2}$
0	2
1	$2\frac{1}{2}$
2	3
3	$3\frac{1}{2}$
4	4

v.

x	y
-3	11
-2	8
-1	5
0	2
1	-1
2	-4
3	-7
4	-10

B.

i.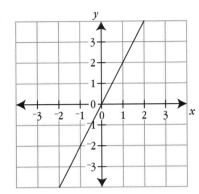

ii.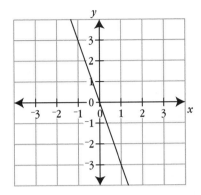

iii.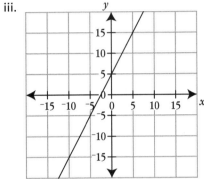

iv.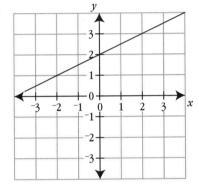

v.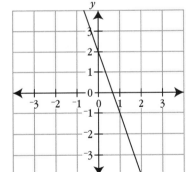

C.
i. ratio = $\frac{2}{1}$ or 2

ii. ratio = $\frac{-3}{1}$ or -3

iii. ratio = $\frac{2}{1}$ or 2

iv. ratio = $\frac{1}{2}$

v. ratio = $\frac{-3}{1}$ or -3

D. The slope is the same as the amount of change between the two values of y compared to the change in the corresponding values of x. The slope is also the same as the coefficient of x in the equations. For example, the ratio for equation i is $\frac{2}{1}$, which is equal to the coefficient 2 in the equation.

Answers to Problem 5.3

A. i.

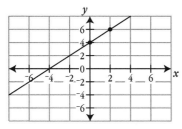

ii.

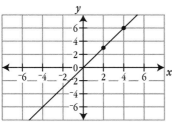

iii.

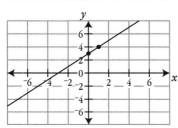

iv.

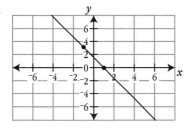

v.

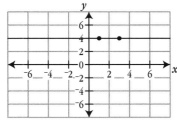

vi.

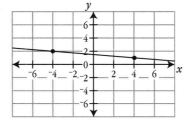

B. i.   increase

ii. increase

iii. increase

iv. decrease

v.   stay the same

vi. decrease

C. i.   slope = 1

ii. slope = $\frac{3}{2}$

iii. slope = 1

iv. slope = $-\frac{3}{2}$

v.   slope = 0 (horizontal line)

vi. slope = $-\frac{1}{8}$

D. Points will vary, but students should verify that the rate of change in the table is the same as the slope.

E. i. y-intercept = 4

ii. y-intercept = 0

iii. y-intercept = 3

iv. y-intercept = $\frac{3}{2}$

v. y-intercept = 4

vi. y-intercept = $\frac{3}{2}$

Answers to Problem 5.3 Follow-Up

3. The change in *x* between two points are not consistent in the table, so you can't just look at the change in the values. To get the slope, you have to find the ratio of the change in *y* over the change in *x*. The ratio between the first two pairs of values is $\frac{34.14 - 31.5}{47.1 - 46} = \frac{2.64}{1.1} = 2.4$; the next ratio is $\frac{36.54 - 34.14}{48.1 - 47.1} = 2.4$; the next is $\frac{38.7 - 36.54}{49 - 48.1} = 2.4$; and the next is $\frac{41.34 - 38.7}{50.1 - 49} = 2.4$. This means that the slope between any two points is 2.4. (Note: This problem is revisited in the next investigation.)

ACE Answers

Applications

18b.
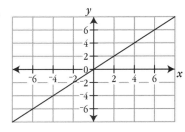

19b.
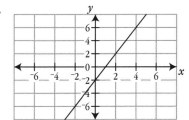

20b.
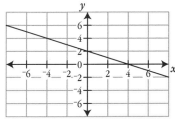

Mathematical Reflections

3. If you know the *y*-intercepts and slopes of two increasing lines, you can picture where they cross the *y*-axis (this is the *y*-intercept) and decide which relationship is rising faster. The line with the greater slope may start lower but will eventually overtake the other line. If the lines are both decreasing, you can make similar comparisons. The line that starts higher may fall below the line that starts lower. The line with the greater slope— in this case the "less negative" slope—will eventually be above the other line. An example is two lines with slopes ⁻5 and ⁻2. The line with slope ⁻5 may be higher on the left of the graph but eventually the line with slope ⁻2 will be above. The same type of reasoning holds for graphs when one has a negative slope and one has a positive slope. The line with the positive slope will eventually be above the line with the negative slope even though for smaller values of *x* the line with negative slope may be above the other.

4. In *Comparing and Scaling*, knowing two ratios allowed us to decide, for example, if a drink mix had a stronger ratio of orange-juice concentrate than another. The relationships between concentrate and water and between concentrate and juice are linear relationships. If we graphed them, they would be straight lines. Stronger concentrations would produce steeper slopes.

Writing an Equation for a Line

In this investigation, students take a look at finding the equation of a line if the slope and *y*-intercept are known. They have already developed several ways to reason about finding the slope of a line given two points. To find the *y*-intercept, they use either a graph or a table.

In Problem 6.1, Solving Alphonso's Puzzle, students find the slope of a line when two points are given, neither of which is the *y*-intercept. In this open-ended problem, they determine the slope by generating a table and looking at the ratio of the differences in *x* and *y* values or by using the ratio of vertical change to horizontal change. They find the *y*-intercept by using rates to generate the point (0, *b*) in the table or by using the graph. Problem 6.2, Converting Temperatures, engages students in writing an equation for converting between Fahrenheit and Celsius temperatures. Problem 6.3, Solving the Mystery of the Irish Elk, presents data about the skull and antler size of an extinct species of elk. Students find an equation that fits the data and use it to make predictions about antler size. This problem previews the ideas about modeling that students will encounter in the grade 8 *Thinking with Mathematical Models* unit.

Mathematical and Problem-Solving Goals

- **To find the equation of a line given two points**

- **To review important ideas about linear relationships**

- **To use knowledge about linear relationships to solve problems**

Materials		
Problem	For students	For the teacher
All	Graphing calculators, grid paper (optional; provided as blackline masters)	Transparencies 6.1 to 6.3 (optional), transparent grids (optional; copy the grids onto transparency film), overhead display model of students' graphing calculator (optional)
6.3		Strips of balsa wood (optional)
ACE	Grid paper (optional)	

Student Pages 80–91   Teaching the Investigation 91a–92

Solving Alphonso's Puzzle

Grouping:
pairs

Launch

■ To introduce the problem, present a similar puzzle for the class to solve. *(optional)*

■ Have students work in pairs on the problem and follow-up.

Explore

■ Circulate as groups work, asking questions about their strategies.

Summarize

■ As students share how they solved the puzzle, look for and highlight the various solution methods.

■ As a class, discuss how to find the slope and *y*-intercept of the line representing the situation.

Assignment Choices

ACE questions 1–13 and unassigned choices from earlier problems

---

INVESTIGATION 6

Writing an Equation for a Line

If you know the slope and the *y*-intercept of a line, it is easy to write an equation of the form $y = mx + b$ for the line. Unfortunately, you are not always given this information. How would you write an equation for a line if you knew only the coordinates of two points on the line? How would you write an equation for a line if you knew only the slope and the coordinates of a point that is not the *y*-intercept? In this investigation, you will work on some interesting problems in which you will consider questions like these.

6.1 Solving Alphonso's Puzzle

Today is Alphonso's birthday. Alphonso's grandfather gave Alphonso some money as a birthday gift. Alphonso says he will put his birthday money in a safe place and add part of his allowance to it each week. His sister Maria asks him how much his grandfather gave him and how much of his allowance he is planning to save each week. As usual, Alphonso does not answer his sister directly. Instead, he gives her some information and lets her puzzle out the answer for herself.

> **Problem 6.1**
>
> **A.** Alphonso tells Maria he will save the same amount from his allowance each week. He says that after five weeks he will have a total of $175 and after eight weeks he will have $190. How much money is Alphonso planning to save each week?
>
> **B.** How much money did Alphonso's grandfather give him for his birthday?

■ **Problem 6.1 Follow-Up**

Write an equation for the total amount of money Alphonso will have saved after a given number of weeks. Describe the reasoning you used to write your equation.

Answers to Problem 6.1

A. $5 per week; In three weeks (week 5 to week 8), Alphonso will have saved $190 – $175 = $15, or $5.

B. Alphonso will have saved 5 × $5 = $25 in the first five weeks, so his starting value must have been $175 – $25 = $150. (Note: Students may have less contextual, more symbolic ways to solve this problem. Or, they may work from a table, applying what they know about relationships with constant rates.)

Answer to Problem 6.1 Follow-Up

$M = 5w + 150$, where M is the amount of money Alphonso has saved and w is the number of weeks; Possible explanations: Alphonso receives $150 to start with, and he adds $5 a week. Or, every linear equation has the form $y = mx + b$, and in this case m (the rate or slope) is 5 and b (the *y*-intercept) is 150.

Detroit, Michigan, is just across the Detroit River from the Canadian city of Windsor, Ontario. Since Canada uses the Celsius temperature scale, weather reports in Detroit often give temperatures in both Fahrenheit and Celsius degrees. The relationship between Fahrenheit degrees and Celsius degrees is linear. In this problem, you will write an equation you can use to convert temperatures from one scale to the other.

Problem 6.2

Two important reference points for temperature are the boiling point and the freezing point of water. Water freezes at 0°C, or 32°F. Water boils at 100°C, or 212°F.

0°C, or 32°F   100°C, or 212°F

Use this information to write an equation for the relationship between Fahrenheit degrees and Celsius degrees.

■ Problem 6.2 Follow-Up

1. Find the *y*-intercept for the equation you wrote in Problem 6.2. What does the *y*-intercept tell you about this situation?

2. Find the slope for the equation you wrote in Problem 6.2. What does the slope tell you about this situation?

3. If it is 85°F outside, what is the Celsius temperature?

4. If it is 30°C outside, what is the Fahrenheit temperature?

At a Glance

Grouping:
small groups

Launch

■ Introduce the problem by having students share their experiences with Celsius and Fahrenheit temperatures.

■ Discuss the variables in the situation and how this problem is similar to others students have worked on.

Explore

■ If students are having trouble finding the slope—either by using a visual representation or by finding the ratio of the difference between the freezing and boiling points of water—help them think about how to find it.

Summarize

■ Ask how students found their equation.

■ Talk about independent and dependent variables. *(optional)*

■ Do the follow-up as a class.

Answer to Problem 6.2

$F = \frac{9}{5}C + 32$ or $C = \frac{5}{9}F - \frac{160}{9}$ (Note: Students may represent this either way. The first representation will probably be more common.)

Answers to Problem 6.2 Follow-Up

1. See page 91g.

2. For the equation $F = \frac{9}{5}C + 32$, the slope is $\frac{9}{5}$ and tells us that the Fahrenheit temperature changes 9° for every 5° change in the Celsius temperature. For the equation $C = \frac{5}{9}F - \frac{160}{9}$, the slope is $\frac{5}{9}$ and tells us that the Celsius temperature changes 5° for every 9° change in the Fahrenheit temperature.

3. $85 = \frac{9}{5}C + 32$, $C = 29.4$°C

4. $F = \frac{9}{5}(30) + 32$, $F = 86$°F

Assignment Choices

ACE questions 14–20, 26, and unassigned choices from earlier problems

Solving the Mystery of the Irish Elk

Launch

- Introduce the story of the Irish elk by discussing the research done to investigate plant and animal species that have become extinct.

- As a class, look at the skull and antler lengths given in the student edition.

- Have groups work on the problem and on the follow-up.

Explore

- As you circulate, offer help to students who need it.

- Ask groups to explain their procedures.

Summarize

- Have students explain how they found the *y*-intercept, then share their solutions to the rest of the problem and the follow-up.

- Discuss the biologists' hypothesis.

Assignment Choices

ACE questions 21–25, 27–30, and unassigned choices from earlier problems

---

6.3 ## Solving the Mystery of the Irish Elk

The data below were gathered by evolutionary biologists studying an extinct animal called the Irish elk. The Irish elk grew to sizes much larger than any modern elk. The biologists were studying fossils to try to find patterns that might help them explain why this animal became extinct.

x	46	47.1	48.1	49	50.1
y	31.5	34.14	36.54	38.7	41.34

Source: *Ever Since Darwin.* Stephen Jay Gould. New York: Norton, 1977. Data have been modified slightly.

The data are skull and antler measurements for five different Irish elk fossils: *x* is the length of the skull in centimeters, and *y* is the length of one antler in centimeters.

In Problem 5.3 Follow-Up, you looked at the data in the above table. You showed that the data are linear and found that the slope of the line that fits the data is 2.4. This means that, for every 1-centimeter increase in the skull length, the antler length increases by 2.4 centimeters. You can use this information to write an equation that describes the relationship between skull length and antler length. Your equation might give you clues about why the Irish elk became extinct.

Problem 6.3

A. Since the relationship represented in the table is linear, its equation can be written in the form $y = mx + b$. You know the slope is 2.4, so the equation becomes $y = 2.4x + b$. Now you need to find the value of b, the y-intercept.

To find b, pick a pair of x and y values from the table, and substitute them into the equation

$$\square = 2.4\square + b$$

What value must b have? Substitute this value into $y = 2.4x + b$ to complete the equation.

B. Use your equation from part A to predict the antler length for a skull length of 55 centimeters.

C. For each Irish elk represented in the table, the antler length is shorter than the skull length. However, the Irish elk skeleton shown on page 82 has antlers much longer than its skull. Can you explain how the skull and antler data for this elk could fit the equation you wrote?

Problem 6.3 Follow-Up

1. Graph the data from the table on a coordinate grid. Use the graph to estimate the y-intercept. Do you get the same y-intercept you found in part A of Problem 6.3?

2. a. Use your graph to predict the antler length for a skull length of 55 centimeters. Do you get the same answer you got by using the equation? Explain.

b. Use the table to predict the antler length for a skull length of 55 centimeters. How does the result compare with the results you got by using the equation and the graph?

Did you know?

The Irish elk was not really an elk, and it wasn't exclusively Irish. It was actually a giant deer that inhabited parts of Europe, Asia, and northern Africa. The Irish elk evolved during the last million years and became extinct about 11,000 years ago. Fossils have been found showing that Irish elk had antlers with spreads of up to 12 feet! These antlers could not have been carried by any modern deer. Indeed, the antlers of the largest Irish elk are so out of proportion with the rest of the skeleton that biologists believe they were an encumbrance rather than an asset.

Investigation 6: Writing an Equation for a Line   83

Answers to Problem 6.3

A. Possible answer: $31.5 = 2.4(46) + b$, so $b = 31.5 - 110.4 = {}^{-}78.9$; The equation is $y = 2.4x - 78.9$. (Note: All of the points will give the same value for the y-intercept.)

B. antler length is $y = 2.4(55) - 78.9 = 53.1$ cm

C. The antler length is greater than the skull length for larger animals. For example, for a skull length of 57 cm, the antler length is $2.4(57) - 78.9 = 57.9$ cm (and the spread of the antlers is about twice this, or 115.8 cm).

Answers to Problem 6.3 Follow-Up

See page 91g.

Answers

Applications

1. $y = {}^-3x + 5$

2. $y = \frac{3}{2}x + 2$

3. $y = x + 1.5$

4. $y = \frac{1}{3}x + \frac{14}{3}$

5. $y = 6$

6. $y = x$

7. $y = \frac{-4}{3}x + 4$

8. $y = {}^-2$

9. $y = \frac{1}{2}x - 1$

As you work on these ACE questions, use your calculator whenever you need it.

Applications

1. Write an equation for the line with slope $^-3$ and y-intercept 5.

2. Write an equation for the line with slope $\frac{3}{2}$ that passes through (0, 2).

3. Write an equation for the line that passes through (0, 1.5) and (1, 2.5).

4. Write an equation for the line that passes through (1, 5) and (4, 6).

5. Write an equation for the line that passes through (2, 6) and (3, 6).

In 6–9, write an equation for the line.

6.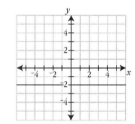

7.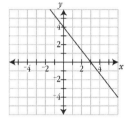

8.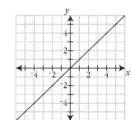

9.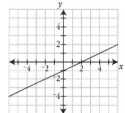

In 10 and 11, write a linear equation that represents the data in the table.

10.

x	−1	0	1	2	3
y	1	3	5	7	9

11.

x	1	2	3	4	5
y	3	2	1	0	−1

12. On the Talk for Less long-distance phone plan, the relationship between the number of minutes a call lasts and the cost of the call is linear. A 5-minute call costs $1.25, and a 15-minute call costs $2.25.

    a. Write an equation for the relationship between the cost and the length of a call.

    b. Find the slope and the y-intercept for the equation, and explain what this information means in the context of this problem.

    c. How much will a 25-minute call cost?

    d. How long can a customer talk for $5.00?

13. The hardware store sells batteries individually. Five batteries cost $4.50, and seven batteries cost $6.30.

    a. Write an equation for the relationship between the cost and the number of batteries.

    b. Find the slope and the y-intercept for the equation, and explain what this information means in the context of this problem.

    c. How much do eight batteries cost?

    d. Dominique spent $10.80 on batteries. How many batteries did she buy?

---

10. $y = 2x + 3$

11. $y = ^-x + 4$

12a. $c = 0.10m + 0.75$, where c is the cost to talk for m minutes

12b. The slope, 0.10, is the rate per minute, and the y-intercept, 0.75, is the initial fee for placing a phone call.

12c. $c = 0.10(25) + 0.75 = 2.50 + 0.75 = \$3.25$

12d. $5.00 = 0.10m + 0.75$
$4.25 = 0.10m$
$42.5 = m$ (42.5 min)

13a. $c = 0.90b$, where c is the cost to buy b batteries

13b. The slope, 0.90, means each battery costs 90¢. The y-intercept, 0, is the cost if no batteries are bought.

13c. $c = 0.90(8) = \$7.20$

13d. $10.80 = 0.90b$
$12 = b$ (12 batteries)

14a. $c = {}^-300p + 350$, where c is the number of cookies sold and p is the price in dollars

14b. The slope, $^-300$, is the rate of decrease (300 cookies) for increasing the price per cookie $1. The y-intercept, 350, is the number of cookies that would "sell" if the price were $0 per cookie. (Note: You may want to discuss with students whether the y-intercept has any real meaning in this context.)

14c. $c = {}^-300(0.70) + 350 = {}^-210 + 350 = 140$ cookies

14d. $300 = {}^-300p + 350$
$^-50 = {}^-300p$
$16.7 = p$ (about 17¢)

15a. $d = 1100t$, where d is the distance in feet to where the lighting struck and t is the time until it is heard

15b. The slope, 1100, is the speed of sound, and the y-intercept, 0, is how far the lightning is from the observer if it is heard after 0 seconds (in other words, if the lightning is seen and heard at the same time). (Note: You may want to ask students what a distance of 0 means in this context.)

15c. 1 mi = 5280 ft, so $5280 = 1100t$, and $t = 4.8$ s

15d. $d = 1100(6\frac{1}{2}) = 7150$ ft or 1.35 mi

---

14. Mr. Brock's class is planning a cookie sale to raise money for the local food bank. They took a survey to help them figure out how much to charge for each cookie. They found that the relationship between the price and the number of cookies they would sell is linear. According to the survey, they will sell about 200 cookies if they charge 50¢, and they will sell about 50 cookies if they charge $1.

a. Write an equation for the relationship between the cost and the number of cookies.

b. Find the slope and the y-intercept for the equation, and explain what this information means in the context of this problem.

c. If they charge 70¢ for each cookie, about how many cookies will they sell?

d. If they want to sell 300 cookies, how much should they charge?

15. You can figure out how far away lightning is by counting the number of seconds between a flash of lightning and the following clap of thunder. The speed of sound is about 1100 feet per second. Thus, if you hear thunder 3 seconds after you see lightning, the lightning hit about $3 \times 1100 = 3300$ feet away.

a. Write an equation you can use to predict the distance lightning is from you from the number of seconds between the lightning and the thunder.

b. Find the slope and the y-intercept for the equation, and explain what this information means in the context of this problem.

c. If lightning hits 1 mile away, how many seconds will elapse before you hear the thunder?

d. If you hear thunder $6\frac{1}{2}$ seconds after you see lightning, how far away did the lightning hit?

16. a. Describe a situation involving a linear relationship whose graph has the given slope.

  i. positive slope   **ii.** negative slope   **iii.** a slope of 0

b. For each situation you described in part a, tell what information the slope and the *y*-intercept give about the situation.

Connections

17. The drawing below shows "trains" of triangles made from toothpicks.

Number of toothpicks	3	5	7
Number of triangles	1	2	3
Perimeter of train	3	4	5

a. Write an equation for the relationship between the number of triangles in a train and the perimeter of the train. Check your equation by testing it on the next few trains in the pattern.

b. Write an equation for the relationship between the number of triangles in a train and the number of toothpicks.

18. Repeat question 17 for trains of squares.

19. Repeat question 17 for trains of hexagons.

(hexagon train drawing)

19a. $p = 4n + 2$, where p is the perimeter and n is the number of hexagons

19b. $t = 5n + 1$, where t is the number of toothpicks and n is the number of hexagons

---

16a. Possible answer: *i (positive slope):* The more time a person spends driving, the farther that person travels. *ii (negative slope):* The more money someone charges for an item, the fewer items she sells. *iii (slope of 0):* If a container is already full when you start to fill it, the volume remains constant.

16b. *i (positive slope):* The slope is the person's driving rate (miles per hour, meters per second), and the *y*-intercept is the distance from a particular spot at the starting time. *ii (negative slope):* The slope is the rate of decrease in number of items sold for increasing the price 1 unit (dollar, penny), and the *y*-intercept is the price that is so high none are sold. *iii (slope of 0):* The slope is the change in volume, and the *y*-intercept is the beginning volume (in this case, the total volume of the container).

Connections

17a. $p = n + 2$, where p is the perimeter and n is the number of triangles; $6 = 4 + 2$, $7 = 5 + 2$, $8 = 6 + 2$

17b. $t = 2n + 1$, where t is the number of toothpicks and n is the number of triangles

18a. $p = 2n + 2$, where p is the perimeter and n is the number of squares

18b. $t = 3n + 1$, where t is the number of toothpicks and n is the number of squares

20. **a.** There is 0.62 mile in 1 kilometer. Write an equation for the relationship between miles and kilometers.

   b. How many miles are in 15 kilometers?

   c. How many kilometers are in 10 miles?

21. In January 1991, a huge oil slick appeared in the Persian Gulf. A couple of days after it was reported, it covered a rectangular area 50 kilometers long and 13 kilometers wide. One day later, it covered a rectangular area 57 kilometers long and 16 kilometers wide.

   a. Assume that the area of the oil slick continued to change at the rate described above. What was the average rate of change of the area of the slick with respect to the number of days? Explain.

   b. Assume the relationship between the area of the slick and time is linear. Write an equation that describes the area of the slick as a function of time.

   c. Draw a graph showing the relationship between area and time.

   d. Estimate how long the oil had been spreading at the time of the first report of its area.

   e. Do you think the oil really spread at a constant rate? Why or why not?

22. The radius of a circular oil spill from a certain underwater drilling site grows at a rate of 10 feet per minute.

   a. Use a table, a graph, and an equation to describe the growth of the radius of the spill over time.

   b. Use a table, a graph, and an equation to describe the growth of the circumference of the spill over time.

   c. Use a table, a graph, and an equation to describe the growth of the area of the spill over time.

   d. Which of the relationships in parts a–c are linear? How did you decide?

21c.

Oil Slick Coverage

y-axis: Area (km²), marked 0, 1000, 2000, 3000, 4000, 5000
x-axis: Time (days), marked 0, 5, 10, 15

23. The distance required to stop a car depends on the speed at which the car is traveling. This stopping distance can be divided into two parts. The *reaction distance* is the distance the car travels from the time the driver realizes there is a need to stop until she applies the brakes. The *braking distance* is the distance the car travels from the moment the brakes are applied until the car stops. The table below shows the reaction distance and the braking distance for travel at different speeds. The *total distance* is the sum of the reaction distance and the braking distance. Below the table, the graphs of reaction distance, braking distance, and total distance are shown on the same set of axes.

Speed (kilometers per hour)	0	20	40	60	80	100	120
Reaction distance (meters)	0	5	10	15	20	25	30
Braking distance (meters)	0	2.5	10	22	40	63	90
Total distance (meters)	0	7.5	20	37	60	88	120

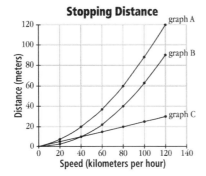

a. Which graph shows the relationship between reaction distance and speed?

b. Which graph shows the relationship between braking distance and speed?

c. Is either relationship linear? Explain your reasoning.

d. Match each equation with its graph.
  i. $d = 0.006s^2$ **ii.** $d = 0.25s$ **iii.** $d = 0.25s + 0.006s^2$

23a. graph c

23b. graph b

23c. No, because the graphs are not straight lines.

23d. i. graph b
ii. graph c
iii. graph a

Extensions

24. $y = \frac{3}{2}x + 3$

25. $y = c$, where c is any constant

26a. $F = 2C + 30$, where C is the Celsius temperature and F is the Fahrenheit temperature

26b. For Celsius temperatures of 10, 15, and 20 degrees, Glenda's rules gives Fahrenheit temperatures of 50, 60, and 70; the equation $F = \frac{9}{5}C + 32$ gives Fahrenheit temperatures of 50, 59, and 68. The results of the two methods are fairly close, although Glenda's rule seems to give slightly higher results at higher temperatures.

26c. See below right.

26d. Answers will vary depending on students' interpretations of "fairly close." Possible answer: Glenda's rule gives results fairly close to those from the equation $F = \frac{9}{5}C + 32$ when the Celsius temperature is between ⁻25°C and 50°C.

27. Possible answers: $y = 5x - 18$, $y = 2x - 9$, $y = \frac{1}{3}x - 4$

28. Possible answers: $y = \frac{3}{2}x + 3$, $y = 6x$, $y = ^-12x + 12$

29. See page 92.

30. See page 92.

Extensions

24. Write an equation of the line that is parallel to the line $y = \frac{3}{2}x + 1$ and has a y-intercept of $(0, 3)$.

25. Write an equation of a line that is parallel to the line $y = 6$.

26. When Glenda travels in Europe, she uses a rule of thumb to convert Celsius temperatures to Fahrenheit temperatures: she doubles the Celsius temperature and adds 30°.

   a. Write an equation for Glenda's rule of thumb.

   b. Convert a few Celsius temperatures to Fahrenheit temperatures, using both Glenda's rule of thumb and the equation you found in Problem 6.2. How do the results of the two conversion methods compare?

   c. Graph the equation for Glenda's rule and the equation from Problem 6.2 on the same set of axes.

   d. For what range of Celsius temperatures does Glenda's rule give Fahrenheit temperatures fairly close to those obtained by applying the equation from Problem 6.2?

27. Write an equation for a line that passes through the point $(3, ^-3)$.

28. Write an equation for a line that passes through the point $(\frac{2}{3}, 4)$.

29. **a.** On a coordinate grid, draw a nonrectangular parallelogram, and write equations for the four lines that contain the sides of the parallelogram.

   b. On a coordinate grid, draw a rectangle, and write equations for the four lines that contain the sides of the parallelogram.

30. **a.** Repeat question 17 for trains of regular, eight-sided polygons.

   b. Repeat question 17 for trains of regular, ten-sided polygons.

   c. Can you make any generalizations about these equations for a figure with any number of sides?

26c.

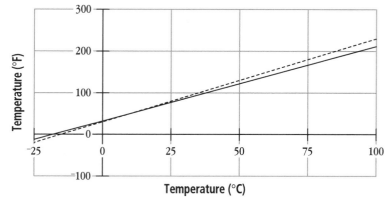

Converting Temperature

Graph with x-axis "Temperature (°C)" ranging from ⁻25 to 100, and y-axis "Temperature (°F)" ranging from ⁻100 to 300. Two lines shown: solid line $F = \frac{9}{5}C + 32$ and dashed line Glenda's rule.

Mathematical Reflections

In this investigation, you learned methods for finding an equation that fits given information. These questions will help you summarize what you have learned:

1. Explain how you can write an equation of a line from the given information. Use examples to illustrate your thinking.

   a. the slope and the y-intercept of the line

   b. two points on the line

   c. the slope of the line and a point on the line that is not the y-intercept

2. Why would you want to write an equation of a line? Use examples to illustrate your answer.

3. In this unit, you did a lot of work with equations. You wrote equations for linear relationships and then used the equations to find solutions and make predictions. Through your work, you probably developed ways to work efficiently with symbols. Apply what you learned to answer these questions.

   a. A student claims that $y = 3x + 10$ and $y = 10 + 3x$ are two ways to represent the same relationship. Do you agree? Why or why not? Can you think of some other ways to represent the relationship $y = 3x + 10$?

   b. What steps would you follow to find the value of y in $y = 10 + 3(^-4)$?

   Think about your answers to these questions, discuss your ideas with other students and your teacher, and then write a summary of your findings in your journal.

Possible Answers

1a. If you have the slope and the y-intercept, you can substitute them into the equation $y = mx + b$. For example, if the slope is 2 and the y-intercept is 3, the equation of the line is $y = 2x + 3$.

1b. See page 92.

1c. See page 92.

2. You might want to calculate other pieces of data without using the approximate method of searching a graph for the point. And you might want to use the equation to have a calculator generate a table, from which you can read any answer you want.

3a. These do represent the same relationship, because numbers can be added in any order and give the same answer, so $3x + 10$ is the same as $10 + 3x$. Some other ways to represent $y = 3x + 10$ are $y = 5 + 5 + 3x$, $y = 1 + 9 + 3x$, and $y = 10 + 2x + x$.

3b. To find the value of y in $y = 10 + 3(^-4)$, I would do the multiplication before the addition: $3(^-4) = ^-12$, and $10 + ^-12 = ^-2$.

Tips for the Linguistically Diverse Classroom

Original Rebus The Original Rebus technique is described in detail in *Getting to Know Connected Mathematics*. Students make a copy of the text before it is discussed. During the discussion, they generate their own rebuses for words they do not understand; the words are made comprehensible through pictures, objects, or demonstrations. Example: Question 3—Key words for which students might make rebuses are *same relationship* (two circles: one with the left half shaded and labeled $y = 3x + 10$, one with the right half shaded and labeled $y = 10 + 3x$), other ways ($y = ?x + ?$).

TEACHING THE INVESTIGATION

6.1 • Solving Alphonso's Puzzle

In this problem students apply what they have learned about linear equations to solve a puzzle.

Launch

You may wish to introduce this problem by presenting a simpler version of Alphonso's puzzle for discussion.

> Alphonso and Maria have a generous grandfather who gives them money on their birthdays. On Maria's last birthday, her grandfather gave her $125, which she intends to save. She also adds $4 each week to this from her weekly allowance. How much money will Maria have after 35 weeks? How many weeks will it take her to save $300?

Prompt the discussion by creating a table and entering the given numbers.

Week	Savings
0	$125
35	
	300

Students will be able to work out missing entries by extending the table or writing a rule. You might ask for the equation of the line.

> What information do we need to find the equation? *(the y-intercept and the slope)* What is the *y*-intercept? *(125)* What is the slope? *(4)* What is the equation that describes this situation? *(y = 4x + 125)*

Pose the problem of Alphonso's birthday present. If you did not discuss Maria's birthday money as an introduction, take the time to read through the introduction and Problem 6.1 with the class, making sure they understand the context.

Have students work on the problem in pairs.

Explore

Circulate as pairs work on the puzzle, asking questions about their methods. Let them think about the problem in whatever way makes sense to them, rather than imposing a particular solution method. Ask them to explain how they are working on the problem and why their strategy makes sense.

> Can you tell me how this relationship would look as a graph? Where would the line cross the *y*-axis? How do you know?

When students finish the problem, have them move on to the follow-up.

Summarize

Ask the class how much money Alphonso is planning to save from his allowance each week and how much his grandfather gave him for his birthday. Have students explain how they found these amounts. Look for different ways of solving the problem. Here are several ways students might solve this problem:

■ Many students will reason verbally. If Alphonso will save $15 in 3 weeks, he must be saving $5 a week. By week 5, he will have saved $25 since his birthday. Therefore, he started with $175 − $25 = $150.

■ Students may construct a table and work out the missing steps to find the rate (the slope). Or, they may use the ratio of vertical change to horizontal change to find the slope. The y-intercept can be found by using the rate to go backward to the point $(0, b)$ in the table.

Week	Savings
0	**$150**
1	**155**
2	**160**
3	**165**
4	**170**
5	175
6	**180**
7	**185**
8	190

■ Students may make a graph and read the rise and run from point to point. On the graph below, the line is extended to give an approximate value for the y-intercept.

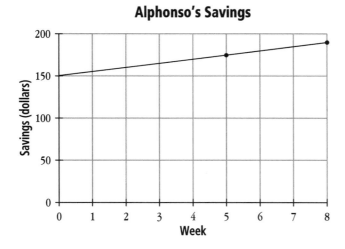

Alphonso's Savings

Move the summary into looking at a more formal way of reasoning about the situation: finding an equation to represent the relationships. Ask how students found the equation for the follow-up, and have them share their strategies.

How did you find the slope? How did you find the y-intercept?

Many students will have noticed that in three weeks, Alphonso will have saved $15. If he saves the same amount every week, he will be saving $5 a week. This is the slope, or the rate at which

Alphonso is saving each week. Some students might find the *y*-intercept by using the idea of the rate. By working backward, they can determine that in the first five weeks, Alphonso will have saved $5 a week for a total of $25. This means he must have started with $175 − $25 = $150. The *y*-intercept is 150.

Because of the understandable context, it is relatively easy for students to reason about the problem to determine the slope and *y*-intercept. If students are given two points that are not in context, it may not be as easy for them to find the slope, the *y*-intercept, and an equation. (Finding the equation of a line in those circumstances will be the subject of an investigation in the grade 8 *Thinking with Mathematical Models* unit.)

6.2 • Converting Temperatures

In this problem, students will derive a formula for converting temperatures between the Celsius and Fahrenheit scales.

Launch

To introduce the context of the problem, have students share their experiences with temperature scales. Present the following scenario:

> If you have traveled in Europe or Canada, you know that temperature is given in Celsius degrees instead of Fahrenheit degrees. Suppose you hear that it is 20° Celsius in Ottawa. How would you interpret how hot or cold it is there?

After students have shared what they know about the relationship between the two scales from their own experience, read the problem with them. The problem gives two points of reference between the two scales: the temperatures at which water boils and freezes.

> What information do we have? *(two temperature readings on two different scales)* How is this problem similar to previous problems? *(We can think of the two temperature readings as two points on a line that represents the relationship between the two scales.)*
>
> What are the variables? *(The temperature given by each scale.)* What would we have to do to graph these two temperature readings? *(decide which variable will be treated as the dependent variable— and thus on the x-axis—and which will be treated as the independent variable—on the y-axis)*

Talk with students about the variables. In this situation, there is no "dependent" variable, because the relationship makes sense either way: you can predict Celsius from Fahrenheit or Fahrenheit from Celsius.

Let students work on the problem and follow-up questions in groups of two or three.

Explore

To write the equation relating the two temperature scales, students will have to find the slope of the line. If they treat Celsius as the variable on the *x*-axis and Fahrenheit as the variable on the *y*-axis, the slope will be $\frac{9}{5}$; treated the other way, it will be $\frac{5}{9}$.

You may need to offer help or give hints to some of the groups. *Students will better understand and remember the concept of the slope if they develop a visual image to represent it,* so you may want to suggest that they graph the relationship to help them to find the vertical and horizontal changes.

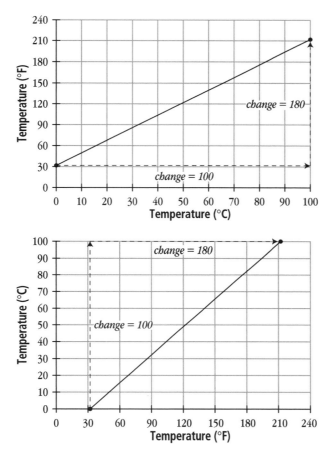

Some students will find the differences between the freezing and boiling points of water for Fahrenheit and Celsius, which are 180°F and 100°C. From these, they can write the ratio $\frac{180}{100}$ and get the slope of 1.8 (or $\frac{100}{180}$ for a slope of 0.56). This is good reasoning as well.

Summarize

Ask how students found their equations. If they chose *C* as the variable on the *x*-axis, writing the equation was probably easier because the numbers were "friendlier" ($F = \frac{9}{5}C + 32$). When *F* is treated as the variable on the *x*-axis, the equation becomes a bit messier ($C = \frac{5}{9}F - \frac{160}{9}$ or $C = 0.56F - 17.8$). It is likely that groups will solve this in different ways; make sure both equations are presented.

This is a good time to explore students' understanding of dependent and independent variables. You might ask whether the Celsius-Fahrenheit relationship $F = \frac{9}{5}C + 32$ (or $F = 1.8C + 32$) shows a relationship in which one variable is dependent on the other:

"If you rewrite this equation as $C = \frac{5}{9}F - \frac{160}{9}$ (or $C = 0.56F - 17.8$), does the dependent variable change?"

You might ask how this relationship differs from the cricket-chirp equation $t = \frac{1}{4}n + 40$ from ACE question 9 in Investigation 4. This equation can also be written as $n = 4t - 160$. In the first equation, temperature depends on the number of chirps. That is, it can be calculated by knowing the number of chirps. In the second equation, the number of chirps depends on the temperature. Both forms of the equation make sense. The one you choose to employ depends on what information you want to find.

Once the class has the equation, help them test it on different temperatures. Have students graph the equation on a calculator. Ask additional questions to check for understanding.

Can you give the coordinates for a third point on the line?

With the class, check a few possibilities for the third point using both equations. Students should be able to offer several.

How many points are on the line? Could we name them all? *(No, because there are an infinite number of points on any line. The equation describes the relationship for the points that lie on the line, and the graph is a picture of this relationship.)*

Ask students the follow-up questions as part of the summary. Talk about whether they used the graphing calculator or the equations to find answers to follow-up questions 3 and 4.

6.3 • Solving the Mystery of the Irish Elk

This real-world problem serves as a review for students to pull together and discuss the various methods they have used to find slopes, *y*-intercepts, and equations of lines. The equation of a line is put to a practical purpose in trying to organize data and make predictions. Plan to spend enough time on this problem so that students see the power that their knowledge of algebra gives them: they can use it to interpret data and to make valuable predictions.

Launch

Introduce the story of the Irish elk by explaining that thousands of plant and animal species that were once on our planet have become extinct and that researchers search for clues to explain their disappearance. In the case of this mammal, researchers found fossils from skeletons of Irish elk of different sizes and used them to generate the data that appears in the student edition. (The data have been altered slightly so students will get a cleaner result for the slope. You may want to explain this to your students, especially if they question why the data have a precisely linear relationship.)

Students will likely expect larger animals to have larger skulls and proportionally larger antlers. However, the ratio of antler length to skull length is not constant in these fossils—though don't point this out to students ahead of time.

Before starting the problem, conduct a short review to help students connect and summarize what they have been working on.

> What does it mean to say that the data are linear?
>
> From the given data, explain how someone could have found that the slope is 2.4. In the context of the Irish elk, what does a slope of 2.4 mean?
>
> If we want to write an equation that represents the information in the table and we know the data are linear and that the slope is 2.4, what else do we need to know? *(the y-intercept)* How could we find the *y*-intercept?

Explain that Problem 6.3 suggests a way to find *b* if we have some data and know the slope. Read through the problem with the class. Have students work in groups of two or three on the problem and follow-up.

Explore

As you circulate, take advantage of the time to give individual attention to students who are struggling. Ask students to explain what they are doing and how they are thinking about the problem.

Summarize

Have students explain how they found the *y*-intercept, *b,* for the Irish elk equation. Have a few students show their work at the board. Try to get students who have chosen different pairs of values and substituted them into the equation. This will help everyone to see that it doesn't matter which pair of values is chosen; they will all produce the same value for *b* (provided it is computed correctly).

Have students share their solutions for part B and the follow-up questions (save part C for later). Ask the class which they prefer—using the table, the graph, or the equation to answer questions 1 and 2—and when it is more convenient to use one method over another.

Talk about part C, and read through the information in the "Did you know?" Seeing the numbers and the picture may not be dynamic enough for students to understand the issue of the antler size. You may want to make models of the skull and antler data and some predicted results. Strips of balsa wood cut to size work well; the wood is inexpensive but doesn't bend like paper. Remember that the spread of the antlers is twice the length of a single antler.

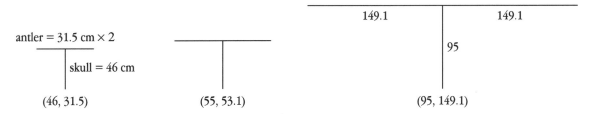

antler = 31.5 cm × 2

skull = 46 cm

(46, 31.5)   (55, 53.1)   (95, 149.1)

149.1   149.1

95

The largest Irish elk fossil specimen has antlers over 150 centimeters long. The skull supporting these 150-centimeter antlers measures only 95 centimeters. (These were large animals!)

Wrap up the discussion by having students discuss whether they agree with the biologists' hypothesis and what they speculate might have been the reason the Irish elk became extinct.

Additional Answers

Answers to Problem 6.2 Follow-Up

1. For the equation $F = \frac{9}{5}C + 32$, the y-intercept is 32 and tells the Fahrenheit temperature when the Celsius temperature is 0. For the equation $C = \frac{5}{9}F - \frac{160}{9}$, the y-intercept is $-\frac{160}{9}$ and tells the Celsius temperature when the Fahrenheit temperature is 0.

Answers to Problem 6.3 Follow-Up

1. Possible answer: The y-intercept is about -80, very close to the exact answer of -78.9.

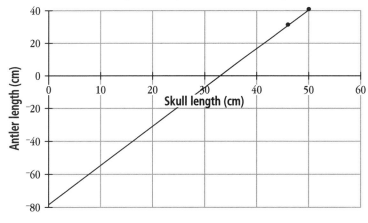

2. a. Possible answer: From my graph, I went up from 55 cm to the line, then across to about 53 cm for the antler length. This is close to the answer I found from the equation, 53.1 cm.

    b. Possible answer: From the table, I calculated the rate of antler growth as 41.34 − 36.54 = 4.8 cm for every 50.1 − 48.1 = 2 cm of skull growth. A skull length of 55 cm is 6 cm longer than a skull length of 49 cm, so the related antler length would be 38.7 + 4.8(3) = 53.1 cm, which is the same answer I got from the equation and close to the answer I got from the graph.

ACE Answers

Connections

22a. $r = 10m$, where r is the radius of the oil spill in feet and m is the number of minutes

Time (minutes)	Radius(feet)
0	0
2	20
4	40
6	60
8	80
10	100
12	120
14	140

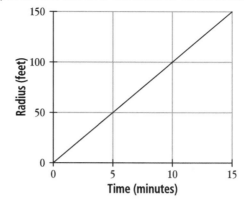

22b. $C = 2\pi r$, with the radius changing at a rate of $10m$, so $C = 2\pi(10m)$ or $C = 20\pi m$

Time (minutes)	Circumference (feet)
0	0
2	125.7
4	251.3
6	377.0
8	502.7
10	628.3
12	754.0
14	879.7

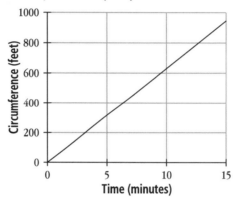

22c. $A = \pi r^2$, with the radius changing at a rate of $10m$, so $A = \pi(10m)^2$ or $A = 100\pi m^2$

Time (minutes)	Area (feet^2)
0	0
2	1257
4	5027
6	11,310
8	20,106
10	31,416
12	45,239
14	61,575

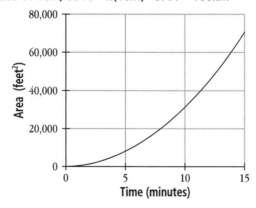

22d. The radius and circumference relationships are linear; the area relationship is not. This can be determined by looking at the graphs, tables, or equations. In the equations, the exponent on the time variable in the linear relationships is 1. In the graphs, the points in the linear relationships connect to make a straight line. In the table, there is a constant change in the dependent variable for each constant change in the independent variable in the linear relationships.

Extensions

29a. Answers will vary. The lines of the parallel sides of the parallelogram should have the same slope. (If the lines are horizontal and vertical, these relationships are not as clear.) Possible answer:

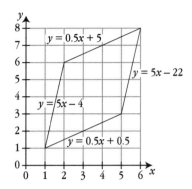

29b. Answers will vary. The lines of the parallel sides of the rectangle should have the same slope, and the lines of the perpendicular sides must have slopes that are negative reciprocals. Possible answer:

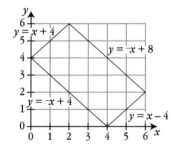

30a. $p = 6n + 2$, where p is the perimeter and n is the number of regular octagons
$t = 7n + 1$, where t is the number of toothpicks and n is the number of regular octagons

30b. $p = 8n + 2$, where p is the perimeter and n is the number of regular decagons
$t = 9n + 1$, where t is the number of toothpicks and n is the number of regular decagons

30c. Students may begin to notice the following pattern: For a figure with n sides, $p = (n - 2)n + 2$ and $t = (n - 1)n + 1$. (Note: Students may not be able to write the formula, but they may be able to recognize and verbalize the patterns.)

Mathematical Reflections

1b. If you know two points on the line, you can find the slope by figuring out what the change in the y value is for a change of 1 in the x value. If one of the points has 0 for the x value, then the y value for that point is the y-intercept. Otherwise, to find the y-intercept, you could graph the points and see where the line crosses the y-axis or figure out what the y value would be for an x value of 0 by seeing how the y values change in relation to the x values. For example, for the points (0, 4) and (2, 6), the slope is 1 (because the y value change is 2 for an x value change of 2), and the y-intercept is 4, so the equation is $y = x + 4$.

1c. If you know the slope of the line and a point that is not the y-intercept, you have to find the y-intercept. You have part of the equation already because you know the slope. Say the slope is 4; then, you know the equation will be $y = 4x + b$. To find the y-intercept, use the point you have and put those values in where x and y are; you will find out what b must be to make the equation work.

Unit Reflections

Working on the problems of this unit you explored many examples of *linear relationships* between variables. You learned how to recognize linear patterns in *graphs* and in *tables* of numerical data and how to express those patterns in words and in symbolic *equations* or *formulas*. Most important of all, you learned how to study tables, graphs, and equations to answer questions about linear relationships. Examples of linear relationships and equations arise in many situations, but there are also important *nonlinear relationships*.

Using Your Algebraic Reasoning—To test your understanding and skill in work with linear relationships, consider some questions that arise in the operation of a movie theater. During daytime hours, the admission prices and operating costs of many theaters are somewhat different from those for ordinary evening hours.

1 *Suppose that a theater charges a school group $4.50 per student to show a special film. Suppose that the theater's operating expenses include $130 for the staff and film rental fee of $1.25 per student.*

a. What equation relates the number of students, x, to the theater's income, I?

b. What equation relates the theater's operating expenses, E, to x?

c. Copy and complete the following table of sample income and expenses for the theater.

Number of Students, x	0	10	20	30	40	50	60	70
Income, I, in dollars								
Expenses, E, in dollars								

d. On the same set of axes, graph both income and operating expenses of the theater for any number of students from 0 to 100.

How to Use
Looking Back and Looking Ahead: Unit Reflections

The first part of this section includes problems that allow students to demonstrate their mathematical understandings and skills. The second part gives them an opportunity to explain their reasoning. This section can be used as a review to help students stand back and reflect on the "big" ideas and connections in the unit. This section may be assigned as homework, followed up with class discussion the next day. Focus on the *Explaining Your Reasoning* section in the discussion. Encourage the students to refer to the problems to illustrate their reasoning.

Using Your Algebraic Reasoning

1a. $I = 4.50x$

b. $E = 1.25x + 130$

c,d. See below.

e. Income: as the number of students, x, increases by 1, income increases by $4.50. Expenses: as the number of students, x, increases by 1, expenses increase by $1.25. For each increase of 10 students, expenses increase by $12.50.

f. Use the answers for part a and part b. Set $I = E$ and solve for x:
$$4.50x = 1.25x + 130$$
$$x = 40$$

2. See page 92c.

---

e. Describe the patterns by which income and operating expenses increase as the number of students increases.

f. Write and solve an equation whose solution will answer the question "How many students need to attend the movie so that the theater's income will equal its operating expenses?"

2 *At another theater, the income and expenses combine to give the equation* $y = 3x - 115$ *relating operating profit, y, to the number of students in a group.*

  a. What do the numbers 3 and −115 tell about

    i. the relation between number of students in a group and the theater's profit?

    ii. the pattern of entries that would appear in a table of sample (students, profit) pairs?

    iii. a graph of the relation between number of students and profit?

  b. Write and solve equations to find the number of students necessary for the theater to

    i. break even (make $0 profit).

    ii. make a profit of $100.

  c. Write and solve an equation that will find the number of students for which the two theaters will make the same profit. Then find the amount of that profit.

Explaining Your Reasoning—When you use mathematical calculations to solve a problem or make a decision, it is important to be able to justify each step in your reasoning.

1. Consider the variables and relationships studied in the two problems.

  a. What are the variables?

  b. Which pairs of variables are related to each other?

  c. In each pair of related variables, how does change in the value of one variable cause change in the value of the other?

2. Which relationships are linear and which are not? What patterns in the tables, graphs, and symbolic rules support your conclusions?

3. For those relationships that are linear, what do the slopes and intercepts of the graphs indicate about the relationships involved?

4. How do the slopes and intercepts relate to data patterns in the various tables of values?

---

1. c.

Number of Students x	0	10	20	30	40	50	60	70
Income, I, in dollars	0	45	90	135	180	225	270	315
Expenses, E, in dollars	130	142.50	155	167.50	180	192.50	205	217.50

1. d.

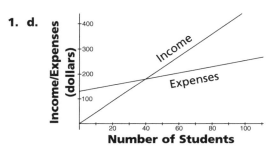

5. Consider the strategies for solving linear equations such as those in Problem 1, part f. and Problem 2, part c.

  a. How can the equations be solved using tables of values?

  b. How can you solve those equations by using the graphs?

  c. How can you solve the equations by reasoning about the equations alone?

6. If you were asked to write a report describing the relationships among number of students, theater income, and operating costs, what value might be gained by including the table? The graph? The equation? What are the limitations of each type of display?

The algebra ideas and techniques you've used in this unit will be applied and extended in many future units of *Connected Mathematics* such as *Thinking with Mathematical Models* and *Say It with Symbols* as well as in work on problems of science and business.

2c. First, find the profit equation for Problem 1 by subtracting expenses from income. Then set this profit equation equal to the profit equation from Problem 2. Solve for x:

$3.25x - 130 = 3x - 115$

$x = 60$

A group of 60 students produces a profit of $65 for either theater.

Note to the Teacher: Since this type of equation is not solved symbolically until *Say It with Symbols,* most students will solve the problem using a graph or table.

Explaining Your Reasoning

See page 92d.

2a. **i.** The purpose of this question is to get students to think about the meaning of the slope and the meaning of the y-intercept. Student answers will vary but the following ideas should be included. "When $x = 0$, there is a loss of $115" and "There is a profit of $3 for every one student."

  ii. Student responses should include the idea that as the number of students, x, increases by one, profit increases by 3.

  iii. Students should say that 3 represents the slope of the line and -115 represents the y-intercept.

  b. **i.** Set the profit equation equal to 0 and solve for x.

$3x - 115 = 0$

$x = 38.33$

So, the number of students needed is 39.

  ii. Set the profit equation equal to 100 and solve for x:

$3x - 115 = 100$

$x = 71.67$

So, the number of students needed is 72.

Since neither the break-even nor the $100-profit figure occurs for a whole number of students, there might be some disagreement about the "right" answers. Common usage assumes an interpretation of the questions as "What is the minimum number of tickets that needs to be sold in order for the theater not to lose money or to realize at least $100 in profit?"

Looking Back and Looking Ahead

Answers

Explaining Your Reasoning

1a. income, expenses, number of students, profit

  b. income-number of students
    expenses-number of students
    profit-number of students
    profit-income
    profit-expenses

  c. Answers will vary. Responses should include the idea that in every case a constant change in the independent variable (x) produces a constant change in the dependent variable (y).

2. All of the relationships are linear. In the tables, the output values (y) change by a constant amount as the input values (x) increase. The graph of each of these relationships is a straight line. The symbolic rule (equation) for each relationship is linear—each contains no exponent larger than one or it is an equation of the form $y = mx + b$.

3. The slopes describe how the output value (y) changes as the input value (x) changes. The y-intercept describes the output value for which the corresponding input value is 0 (where the line intersects the x-axis). The x-intercept describes the input value for which the y-value is 0 (where the line intersects the x-axis).

4. The slopes describe the constant rate of change in the output (y) as the input (x) changes. In the tables, the x-intercepts will be the ordered pairs for which $y = 0$ and the y-intercepts will be the ordered pairs for which $x = 0$.

5a. In Problem 1f, make tables of values for the income and expense expressions and look for a value of x that makes the two expressions equal.
In Problem 2c, write profit expressions for each theater as income minus expenses. Then produce tables of values for each profit expression and look for values of x that make the two expressions equal.

  b. Graph both equations on the same coordinate grid and find the point of intersection.

  c. Set the income and expense expressions equal to one another and solve for x.

6. The purpose of this question is to get students to think about the various useful mathematical tools that they are acquiring and when each is most useful. Varied answers often mention that a graph gives a quick overall picture of a relationship, a table gives specific numerical information more directly, and a formula gives a tool for calculating outputs for any input.

Assessment Resources

Grid paper and graphing calculators should be available to students for use during the check-up, quizzes, and questions from the Question Bank. All students will need a sheet of graph paper for use on Quiz A and the Unit Test.

Check-Up

1. Find four matches among the equations, tables, graphs, and the situation. On the lines below, write the letters that make up your matches.

_____   _____   _____   _____

A	
x	y
0	100
1	105
2	110
3	115
4	120
5	125

B	
x	y
0	0
1	5
2	10
3	15
4	20
5	25

C	
x	y
0	0
1	20
2	40
3	60
4	80
5	100

D

Troy's group did the leaking-faucet experiment and found that the cup leaked water at a rate of 5 ml per second.

E

$$y = x + 5$$

F

$$y = 5x + 100$$

G

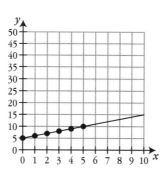

H

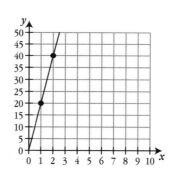

2. Which table in question 1 shows the greatest rate of change? Explain how you know.

Check-Up

3. Which graph in question 1 shows the greater rate of change? Explain how you know.

4. Which equation in question 1 shows the greater rate of change? Explain how you know.

Quiz A

1. **a.** Which table or tables show the patterns of a linear relationship?

Table A	
x	*y*
⁻3	3
⁻2	2
⁻1	1
0	0
1	1
2	2
3	3

Table B	
x	*y*
⁻3	⁻7
⁻2	⁻5
⁻1	⁻3
0	⁻1
1	1
2	3
3	5

Table C	
x	*y*
⁻3	1
⁻2	$1\frac{2}{3}$
⁻1	$2\frac{1}{3}$
0	3
1	$3\frac{2}{3}$
2	$4\frac{1}{3}$
3	5

   b. Describe how you decided whether the relationship between the variables in each table was linear.

2. The graph to the right shows gallons of gas consumed by Jake's car compared to distance traveled.

   a. What would it mean in this situation if the line were steeper than shown and the scales on the graph stayed the same?

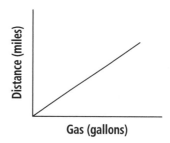

   b. Put a sensible scale on the axes, and write a question that can be answered from your graph. Show where the answer can be found on your graph.

Quiz A

In 3–6, use this information: Matthias has a summer job as a lifeguard earning $6.00 an hour. Jill has a summer job as a carpenter's helper earning $5.50 an hour.

3. How many hours does each student have to work to make $200.00? Show all the work you do to find your solution.

4. If they both work 25 hours, how much more money will Matthias earn than Jill? Show your work.

5. It takes Jill 23 hours to earn $126.50. How long will it take Matthias to earn that much? Show your work.

6. For each student's salary, write an equation that you could enter into a graphing calculator that shows how that student's pay is related to the number of hours he or she works.

7. These three equations were offered as possible walkathon pledge plans.

   $y = 1.5x$ $y = 15 + 0.25x$ $y = 0.50x + 2$

   a. Choose the equation you think is most reasonable for a pledge plan. Explain why you chose that equation and how the numbers in the equation affect the payment for the walkathon.

   b. Make a table that shows how much money a sponsor would pay, using your chosen rule, for a participant walking up to 10 miles.

   c. Make a graph of the rule you chose. Be sure to label the scales of your axes.

Quiz A

8. Match each table with a graph and an equation. On the lines below, write the letters that make up your matches.

_____   _____   _____   _____

A			E		I
			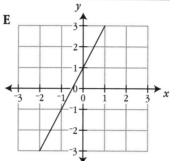		$y = -x + 1$

A

x	y
−2	−5
−1	−3
0	−1
1	1
2	3

E

I

$y = -x + 1$

B

x	y
−2	3
−1	2
0	1
1	0
2	−1

F

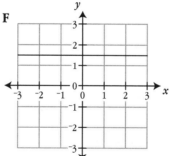

J

$y = 2x + 1$

C

x	y
−2	1.5
−1	1.5
0	1.5
1	1.5
2	1.5

G

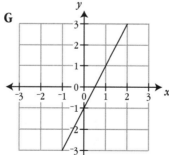

K

$y = 1.5$

D

x	y
−2	−3
−1	−1
0	1
1	3
2	5

H

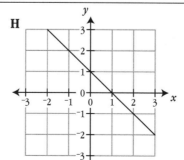

L

$y = 2x - 1$

Quiz B

Henri has been walking every day and has increased his speed. He now walks at a rate of 2 meters per second. Emile has not been practicing but finds that he can still walk at a rate of 2.5 meters per second. Emile and Henri decide to have another race. Emile gives his brother a head start of 40 meters.

1. Write an equation for each brother that shows the relationship between distance walked and time.

Use graphs, tables, or your equations to answer questions 2–5. In each question, *sketch* the section of graph (with the scale marked) or the table and indicate where you found the answer, or *record* the computational work you do.

2. Find each brother's distance at 60 seconds.

3. Find the time when Emile catches up with his brother.

4. What are the *y*-intercepts? Explain how you can find the *y*-intercepts in each representation—table, graph, and equation.

Quiz B

5. What is the slope of the line represented by each brother's walking rate? Explain how you can find the slope in each representation: table, graph, and equation.

In 6–9, find the value of the indicated variable.

6. Find x if $10 = x - 2.5$.

7. Find y if $y = 7 + 5.25(5)$.

8. Find x if $922.5 = 45x$.

9. Find x if $^-12 = 22x - 100$.

10. Explain how you found x in question 8.

11. Explain how you found x in question 9.

12. Each equation in questions 6–9 is a specific case of a linear equation of the form $y = mx + b$. For question 6, find the slope and the y-intercept for the equation $10 = x - 2.5$.

Assign these questions as additional homework, or use them as review, quiz, or test questions.

1. Brent's Video Shack charges $1.50 to rent a video game for a night. Mr. Buck's Entertainments opens a new store in town, charging $1.00 per night for a game, and starts to take customers away from Brent's Video Shack.

    a. Graph each price scheme on the same set of axes.

    b. How could Brent change his charges, so that he includes a one-time membership fee and drops his rental fee below Mr. Buck's, to get his customers back without losing too much money? Graph your proposal, and explain to Brent how it will work.

2. Does it make a difference what two points you choose on a straight line to find the slope of the line? Explain your answer.

3. Big A's Bike Rentals charges $300 plus $20 per bike to rent bikes for a week. Little Cheeper's rental shop charges $50 plus $35 per bike for a week. You need to determine which company to use for your bike-touring project. Write an explanation to a student who has never used a graphing calculator to help that student display and solve this problem on a graphing calculator.

4. Gretchen was absent when the class worked through Investigation 4. Write an explanation to her about how to solve equations using the symbolic method. Use the equation $4n - 17 = 43$ as an example.

5. a. This table shows two points that are on the same straight line. Complete the table to show three other points on the same line.

x	$^-3$				1
y	$^-2$				6

    b. Find the slope and the y-intercept of this line.

6. Given one of the representations below, find the other two.

Table	Graph	Equation
x y -2 14 0 8 1 5 2 2 3 -1		
	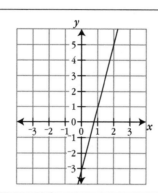	
		$y = \frac{1}{3}x + 1$

a. Find the y-intercept for each representation above.

b. Find the slope for each representation above.

7. Sam made up a set of tables based on some equations. He gave the tables to Adrian and challenged her to find the equations for each table. Adrian added two columns to each table to help her find the equations. Below is the start of her work.

Table A

Diff. x	x	y	Diff. y
none	$^-2$	$^-1$	
1	$^-1$	1	
	0	3	
	1	5	
	2	7	

Table B

Diff. x	x	y	Diff. y
	$^-3$	$^-8$	
	$^-1$	0	
	1	0	
2	3	$^-8$	
	5	$^-24$	

Table C

Diff. x	x	y	Diff. y
	$^-3$	$^-\frac{1}{2}$	
	$^-1$	$\frac{1}{2}$	1
	0	1	
	3	2.5	
	5	3.5	

Table D

Diff. x	x	y	Diff. y
	$^-2$	$^-5$	
	$^-1$	$^-3$	
	0	$^-1$	
	1	1	2
	2	3	

a. Adrian used the extra columns to find the differences in x values and y values. Complete these columns for each table.

b. Describe any patterns you see in the columns of differences.

c. Find the equation of any table that represents a linear relationship.

d. Explain why Adrian added the columns to the tables Sam gave her. Do you think it helped her to find the equations? Explain your thinking.

8. The formula relating n (the number of cricket chirps per minute) to t (the temperature in degrees Fahrenheit) is $n = 4t - 160$.

a. Using a symbolic method, find how many times a cricket would chirp in a minute at 90°F.

b. It is evening, and a cricket is chirping 48 times per minute. Use a symbolic method to find the temperature.

Unit Test

1. The organizers of a walking race want the racers to finish close together, so some of the racers will be given head starts. The organizers wrote the equation $y = 40 + 2x$ for one racer and entered it into a graphing calculator. They highlighted one point on their graph, which is shown at the right.

   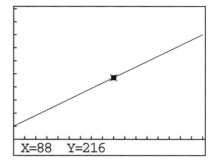

   X=88   Y=216

   a. What question could the organizers be trying to solve from the graph?

   b. Write your question from part a as an equation. (Be sure the equation has one variable.)

   c. Solve the equation you wrote in part b by using a symbolic method. Does your answer agree with the graphical method? Explain.

Unit Test

2. Scientists have found that there is a linear relationship between cricket chirps and temperature, and they have come up with the equation relating cricket chirps to temperature. If you time the first cricket you hear on a cool morning, you might find that the number of chirps is 40 per minute. At noon, the cricket may be chirping at a rate of 160 chirps per minute. These values have been entered into the table below.

Chirps	40	160
Temperature (°F)	50	80

a. Complete the table to show the temperature when the number of chirps is 50, 60, 70, . . . , 150.

Chirps	40	50	60	70	80	90	100	110	120	130	140	150	160
Temp. (°F)	50												80

b. What is the temperature when the number of chirps is 0? Explain how you found your answer.

c. What is the increase in temperature when the number of chirps increases by 1?

d. Using this information, find the equation giving the temperature for any number of cricket chirps. Explain what each number in your equation means.

Unit Test

In 3–5, use this information: You have worked with equations for finding the circumference and area of circles. These rules can be written as follows:

$$C = \pi d \quad \text{or} \quad C = 2\pi r$$

$$A = \pi r^2$$

where C is the circumference, r is the radius, d is the diameter, π represents the value pi, and A is the area.

3. For each equation, fill in the table with five pairs of numbers.

    a. $C = \pi d$

d					
C					

    b. $C = 2\pi r$

r					
C					

    c. $A = \pi r^2$

r					
A					

4. On a sheet of graph paper, make a graph for each rule.

5. Which of the rules represent a linear relationship?

    a. How can you tell from the tables?

    b. How can you tell from the graphs?

    c. How can you tell from the equations?

Unit Test

In 6–10, use this information: In the bouncing-ball experiment, Aimee used a ball with a super-high bounce and collected lots of data. The data suggest that there is a linear relationship between the drop height and the bounce height, and the data points seem to lie on a line. Aimee graphs two of her data points and draws a line through them. With these two points, she finds the equation of the line.

Data Points

(drop height in cm, bounce height in cm)

(60, 90)
(30, 45)

Graph

Bounce Height

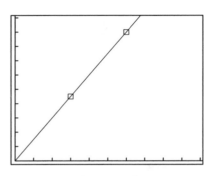

Drop Height

6. What is the slope of the line? Explain how you worked this out.

7. What is the *y*-intercept of the line? Explain how you worked this out.

8. What is the equation of the line?

9. Use the equation to predict the bounce height if the drop height is 10 meters.

10. Use the equation to predict the drop height if the ball bounces 10 meters.

Notebook Checklist

Journal Organization

_____ Problems and Mathematical Reflections are labeled and dated.

_____ Work is neat and is easy to find and follow.

Vocabulary

_____ All words are listed.　　_____ All words are defined or described.

Check-Up and Quizzes

_____ Check-Up

_____ Quiz A

_____ Quiz B

Homework Assignments

_____ _____

_____ _____

_____ _____

_____ _____

_____ _____

_____ _____

_____ _____

_____ _____

_____ _____

_____ _____

_____ _____

_____ _____

_____ _____

_____ _____

Self-Assessment

Vocabulary

Of the vocabulary words I defined or described in my journal, the word _____ best demonstrates my ability to give a clear definition or description.

Of the vocabulary words I defined or described in my journal, the word _____ best demonstrates my ability to use an example to help explain or describe an idea.

Mathematical Ideas

Relationships between variables sometimes show a predictable pattern. For some relationships, as one variable changes by a unit amount, the other variable changes at a constant rate. This is known as a *linear relationship*.

1. **a.** After studying the mathematics in *Moving Straight Ahead*, I learned the following things about how linear relationships in tables, graphs, and equations are displayed:

    b. Here are page numbers of journal entries that give evidence of what I have learned, along with descriptions of what each entry shows:

2. **a.** These are the mathematical ideas I am still struggling with:

    b. This is why I think these ideas are difficult for me:

    c. Here are page numbers of journal entries that give evidence of what I am struggling with, along with descriptions of what each entry shows:

Class Participation

I contributed to the class discussion and understanding of *Moving Straight Ahead* when I . . . (Give examples.)

Answer Keys

Answers to the Check-Up

1. A and F, B and D, C and H, E and G

2. Table C shows the greatest rate of change. The values for x increase by 1 in all three tables, but the y values increase the most (by 20) in table C.

3. Graph H shows the greater rate of change. The scales on the x-axes are the same, so the line that is steeper—graph H—has the greater slope.

4. Equation F shows the greater rate of change. The equation with the greater coefficient of x has the greater rate of change, and that is equation F with a coefficient of 5. (Note: Students might choose equation F and say that the constant 100 is what causes the rate of change. This is the correct answer but the wrong reason.)

Answers to Quiz A

1. a. tables B and C

   b. In table B the values of y increase by 2 for every increase of 1 in x. In table C the values of y increase by $\frac{2}{3}$ for every increase of 1 in x. In table A the y values decrease by 1 and then increase again. A constant rate of increase in the dependent variable signals a linear relationship.

2. a. A steeper line would mean that more distance was traveled per gallon of gas, indicating a better gas mileage.

   b. Possible answer: How many miles can Jake travel if he has 3 gallons of gas in his tank? On the graph shown, the answer is approximately 80 miles. (Note: Check that students have tried to mark off the scale with constant intervals and that their answers match the scale they chose.)

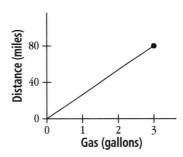

3. Matthias has to work $\frac{200}{6} = 33.3$ h. Jill has to work $\frac{200}{5.5} =$ about 36.4 h.

4. Matthias earns $25 \times 6 = \$150$. Jill earns $25 \times 5.5 = \$137.50$. Matthias earns $150 - 137.50 = \$12.50$ more than Jill.

5. Matthias will have to work $\frac{126.50}{6} =$ about 21.08 h, or a little over 21 h.

6. Matthias: $y = 6x$, Jill: $y = 5.5x$

7. a. Possible answer: $y = 1.5x$; For each mile walked, the participant would collect $1.50 from each sponsor. The other two rules have the participant collecting less per mile (25¢ or 50¢) but also collecting a flat amount at the start from each sponsor ($15 or $2).

b.

$y = 1.5x$		$y = 15 + 0.25x$		$y = 0.50x + 2$	
x	**y**	**x**	**y**	**x**	**y**
0	$0.00	0	$15.00	0	$2.00
1	1.50	1	15.25	1	2.50
2	3.00	2	15.50	2	3.00
3	4.50	3	15.75	3	3.50
4	6.00	4	16.00	4	4.00
5	7.50	5	16.25	5	4.50
6	9.00	6	16.50	6	5.00
7	10.50	7	16.75	7	5.50
8	12.00	8	17.00	8	6.00
9	13.50	9	17.25	9	6.50
10	15.00	10	17.50	10	7.00

c.

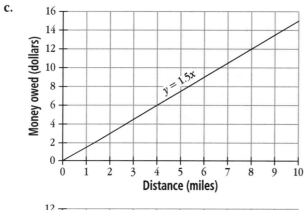

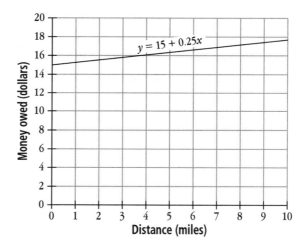

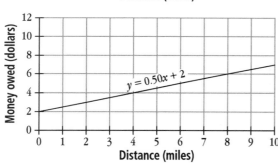

8. A, G, and L; B, H, and I; C, F, and K; D, E, and J

Answers to Quiz B

1. Emile: $y = 2.5x$, Henri: $y = 2x + 40$

2. Emile: $y = 2.5(60) = 150$ m, Henri: $y = 2(60) + 40 = 160$ m

3. This can be done graphically or with a table.

X	Y₁	Y₂
77	192.5	194
78	195	196
79	197.5	198
80	200	200
81	202.5	202
82	205	204
83	207.5	206

X=80

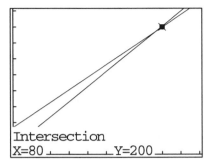

Intersection
X=80   Y=200

In the table, the equation values (represented by Y_1 and Y_2) are the same when $x = 80$. Emile catches up with Henri after 80 s. In the graph, the lines representing the boys' equations intersect when Emile catches up with Henri, which happens at 80 s.

4. The y-intercept for Emile's equation is 0. It can be found from the equation by noticing that no constant is added to $2.5x$. In the graph, it can be determined by finding where the line crosses the y-axis—it goes through the origin, which has a y value of 0. In the table, it can be found by looking at the row for when $x = 0$; at that point, $y = 0$. The y-intercept for Henri's equation is 40. It can be found from the equation by noticing that a constant of 40 is added to $2x$. In the graph, it can be determined by finding where the line crosses the y-axis. In the table, it can be found by looking at the row for when $x = 0$; at that point, $y = 40$.

5. The slope for Emile's line is 2.5; the slope for Henri's line is 2. In the equations, the slope is the coefficient of x. In the graphs, the slope can be found by using two points that lie on the line and calculating the amount of rise divided by the amount of the run between them (this is the least efficient method and the one in which mistakes are the most common). In the tables, the slope can be found by looking at the y values of two x values that have a difference of 1. The slope is equal to the difference between the two y values (subtracting the y value corresponding to the smaller x value from the y value corresponding to the greater x value).

6. $x = 12.5$

7. $y = 33.25$

8. $x = 20.5$

9. $x = 4$

10. Possible answer: In the equation $922.5 = 45x$, the number represented by x must be multiplied by 45 to get 922.5. That means that if you were to divide 922.5 by 45, you would find the value of x: $x = \frac{922.5}{45} = 20.5$. (Note: This answer uses the idea of inverse operations.)

11. Possible answer: In the equation $^-12 = 22x - 100$, the number represented by x must be multiplied by 22 and decreased by 100 to get an answer of $^-12$. That means that if you were to add 100 to $^-12$ and divide the sum by 22, you would find the value of x: $x = \frac{^-12 + 100}{22} = 4$. (Note: Again, inverse operations is a reasonable way for students to explain how they found x.)

12. The equation $10 = x - 2.5$ is a specific case of the equation $y = x - 2.5$, which has a slope of 1 and a y-intercept of $^-2.5$.

Answers to the Question Bank

1. **a.**

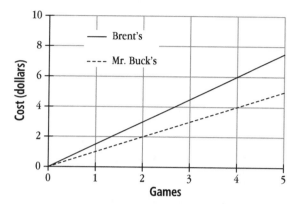

b. Possible answer: Brent might charge a membership fee of $5 and then $0.50 per game per night. For the first 10 games, Brent's customers will pay more, but after 10 games their total cost will be lower than if they rented from Mr. Buck's. Brent should advertise his plan, emphasizing that if you are frequent customer you will be better off at Brent's.

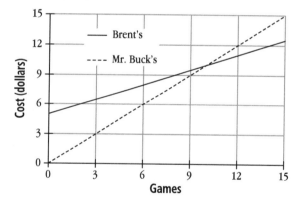

2. It does not matter which two points you use to determine the slope of a straight line. Since there is a constant rate of change between any two points on a straight line, the slope is the same between any two points on that line.

3. On the appropriate screen you need to enter the equations $Y_1 = 300 + 20X$ and $Y_2 = 50 + 35X$, where X represents the number of bikes. Next you need to set a window appropriate for the context, maybe x values from 0 to 20 and y values corresponding to these, say from 0 to 700. When you graph these equations, you will see two lines giving the costs for the two companies. The point where the lines cross is the point where the two plans cost the same for that number of bikes. Before or after that point, one company or the other has the better deal.

4. You can think of solving an equation like this one as reversing the procedure that was done to create the expression on the left. To make $4n - 17$ you would multiply n by 4 and then subtract 17. To reverse this, you add 17, then divide by 4.

$$4n - 17 = 43$$
$$4n - 17 + 17 = 43 + 17$$
$$4n = 60$$
$$\frac{4n}{4} = \frac{60}{4}$$
$$n = 15$$

5. a.

x	$^-3$	$^-2$	$^-1$	0	1
y	$^-2$	0	2	4	6

b. slope $= \frac{2}{1} = 2$, y-intercept $= 4$

6.

Table	Graph	Equation
 <table><tr><td>x</td><td>y</td></tr><tr><td>$^-2$</td><td>14</td></tr><tr><td>0</td><td>8</td></tr><tr><td>1</td><td>5</td></tr><tr><td>2</td><td>2</td></tr><tr><td>3</td><td>$^-1$</td></tr></table>	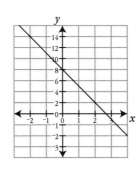	$y = {}^-3x + 8$
<table><tr><td>x</td><td>y</td></tr><tr><td>0</td><td>$^-3$</td></tr><tr><td>1</td><td>1</td></tr><tr><td>2</td><td>5</td></tr></table>	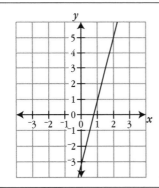	$y = 4x - 3$
<table><tr><td>x</td><td>y</td></tr><tr><td>$^-2$</td><td>$\frac{1}{3}$</td></tr><tr><td>$^-1$</td><td>$\frac{2}{3}$</td></tr><tr><td>0</td><td>1</td></tr><tr><td>1</td><td>$1\frac{1}{3}$</td></tr><tr><td>2</td><td>$1\frac{2}{3}$</td></tr></table>	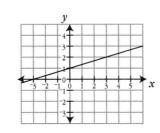	$y = \frac{1}{3}x + 1$

a. The y-intercepts are 8, $^-3$, and 1.

b. The slopes are $^-3$, 4, and $\frac{1}{3}$.

7. a.

	Table A		
Diff. x	x	y	Diff. y
none	$^-2$	$^-1$	none
1	$^-1$	1	2
1	0	3	2
1	1	5	2
1	2	7	2

	Table B		
Diff. x	x	y	Diff. y
none	$^-3$	$^-8$	none
2	$^-1$	0	8
2	1	0	0
2	3	$^-8$	$^-8$
2	5	$^-24$	$^-16$

	Table C		
Diff. x	x	y	Diff. y
none	$^-3$	$^-\frac{1}{2}$	none
2	$^-1$	$\frac{1}{2}$	1
1	0	1	$\frac{1}{2}$
3	3	2.5	1.5
2	5	3.5	1

	Table D		
Diff. x	x	y	Diff. y
none	$^-2$	$^-5$	none
1	$^-1$	$^-3$	2
1	0	$^-1$	2
1	1	1	2
1	2	3	2

b. In tables A and D, x and y increase by constant amounts. In table B, x increases by increments of 2, but y increases and then decreases by different amounts. In table C, x and y increase by different amounts but the ratio of the increments is always $\frac{1}{2}$—that is, the ratio $\frac{\text{increment in } y}{\text{increment in } x} = \frac{1}{2}$.

c. table A: $y = 2x + 3$
table C: $y = \frac{1}{2}x + 1$
table D: $y = 2x - 1$

d. Adrian added the columns to help her look at how the increments in the y values changed in relation to how the increments in the x values changed. In linear relationships, these changes will both be constant. Once Adrian had determined which of the tables represented linear relationships, she could find the related equations, because the ratio of the increments is the slope of the line.

8. a. $n = 4t - 160 = 4(90) - 160 = 360 - 160 = 200$ chirps per minute

b.
$$48 = 4t - 160$$
$$48 + 160 = 4t - 160 + 160$$
$$208 = 4t$$
$$\frac{208}{4} = \frac{4t}{4}$$
$$52 = t$$
The temperature is 52°F.

Answers to the Unit Test

1. a. Possible answers: They could be trying to find out how long it would take until the walker was 216 meters from the starting line. Or, they could be trying to find out how far the walker will be from the starting line after 88 seconds.

b. Possible answers: The equation for finding out how long it would take until the walker was 216 meters from the start is $216 = 40 + 2x$. The equation for finding how far the walker will be from the start after 88 seconds is $y = 40 + 2(88)$.

c.
$$216 = 40 + 2x$$
$$216 - 40 = 40 - 40 + 2x$$
$$176 = 2x$$
$$\frac{176}{2} = \frac{2x}{2}$$
$$88 = x$$

(This agrees with the graphical method in that the solution that was arrived at above is also the value for x that corresponds with the value of 216 for y on the graph.)

$$y = 40 + 2(88)$$
$$y = 40 + 176$$
$$y = 216$$

(This agrees with the graphical method in that the solution that was arrived at above is also the value for y that corresponds with the value of 88 for x on the graph.)

2. a.

Chirps	40	50	60	70	80	90	100	110	120	130	140	150	160
Temp. (°F)	50	52.5	55	57.5	60	62.5	65	67.5	70	72.5	75	77.5	80

b. When the number of chirps is 0, the temperature is 40°F. This can be obtained by continuing the table to the left by subtracting 2.5 from each temperature to find the one immediately preceding it.

Chirps	0	10	20	30	40
Temp. (°F)	40	42.5	45	47.5	50

c. In the table, when the number of chirps increases by 10, the temperature increases by 2.5. To find the temperature increase for an increase of only 1 chirp, we can divide this interval into 10 smaller intervals and divide the 2.5°F change into 10 intervals for a change of 0.25°F.

d. Let c = chirps per minute and t = temperature in degrees Fahrenheit. Then, $t = 40 + 0.25c$ (or $t = 40 + \frac{1}{4}c$ or $t = 40 + \frac{c}{4}$). The y-intercept, 40, is the temperature when the number of chirps is 0. The slope, 0.25, represents how much the temperature increases for an increase of 1 in the number of chirps per minute.

3. a. Possible table (using 3.14 for π):

d	1	2	3	4	5
C	3.14	6.28	9.42	12.56	15.7

b. Possible table:

r	1	2	3	4	5
C	6.28	12.56	18.84	25.12	31.4

c. Possible table:

r	1	2	3	4	5
A	3.14	12.56	28.26	50.24	78.5

4.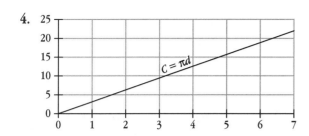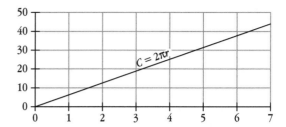

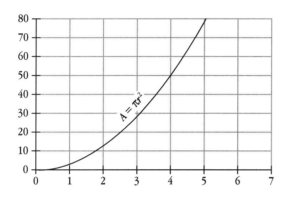

5. $C = \pi d$ and $C = 2\pi r$ represent linear relationships.

    a. This can be seen from the tables by looking at consecutive values for C. The differences between these values is always constant.

    b. This can be seen from the graphs by noticing that they are straight lines.

    c. This can be seen from the equations by seeing that the variable d (or r) is only multiplied by a constant, π (or 2π), not by itself (as in $A = \pi r^2$).

6. $\frac{3}{2}$ or 1.5; Possible explanation: I calculated the change in the y values ($90 - 45 = 45$) and divided by the change in the x values ($60 - 30 = 30$).

7. $(0, 0)$; Possible explanation: Another point that would have to lie on this line can be found by continuing the progression of x and y values. There is a constant difference of 30 in the x values and 45 in the y values. Subtracting these differences from the point $(30, 45)$ gives the point $(0, 0)$, which is the y-intercept.

8. $y = 1.5x$, where $y =$ bounce height and $x =$ drop height.

9. 10 m = 1000 cm, and bounce height is $y = 1.5(1000) = 1500$ cm (or 15 m)

10. $1000 = 1.5x$

    $\frac{1000}{1.5} = \frac{1.5x}{1.5}$

    $666.7 = x$, so the drop height $= 666\frac{2}{3}$ cm or 6.67 m

The assessment for *Moving Straight Ahead* includes a check-up and two partner quizzes. Below are scoring rubrics, grading scales, and samples of student work provided by a teacher using the Connected Mathematics curriculum for the check-up and Quiz B. These are offered as examples of how you might assess your students' work.

Scoring the Check-Up

In this class, students worked on this assessment individually.

Point Rubric

A total of 9 points was assigned by this teacher to this assessment task.

3 points for question 1
- 3 points for all pairs correct
- 2 points for two correct pairs
- 1 point for one correct pair

Rationale for this point distribution: If you have three of the four pairs correct, you must have the fourth. If you miss one pair, you must have missed another. To give each pair 1 point would double-penalize students, as they can't miss just a single pair.

6 points for questions 2, 3, and 4
- 2 points for each complete explanation
- 1 point for each partially correct and complete explanation

Grading Scale

Points	Grade
8 to 9	A
6 to 7	B
5	C
4	D

Sample 1

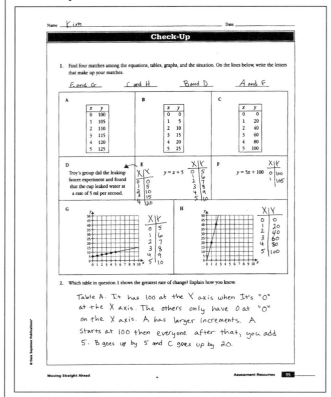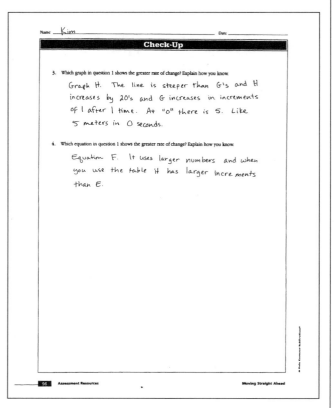

Teacher's Comments on Kim's Check-Up

Kim earned 8 of the 9 points given for this check-up. For question 1 she correctly pairs the given equations, tables, graphs, and written descriptions. For question 2, Kim identifies the wrong table as being the one with the greatest rate of change. She is confused between the amount of change and the values for the variables when a constant is added. She earned 1 of the 2 points because in her last sentence she states each of the rates of change when she talks about what each table "goes up by." For question 3 she earned both points, although her explanation for the y-intercept being 5 is not reasonable. What she has written implies that she has made sense of graphs, and that if the scales are the same then the steepness of the line is important in determining the rate of change. She also makes sense of the rate of change by talking about the size of the increments. For question 4 Kim earned both points, though her explanation is a bit confusing. She identifies the correct equation but it is unclear what she means by "larger numbers." Based on her explanation in question 2, one could conclude that she is referring to the constant 100. The table that she made on page 1, next to each of the equations, explains where she came up with the information about increments. Kim shows no evidence of linking the coefficient of x to the rate of change. That is fine at this point; it is an idea that has only been hinted at in discussions during the unit and will come up again in later investigations. The check-up indicates to me that Kim has made enough sense of the skills introduced so far in this unit to move on.

Sample 2

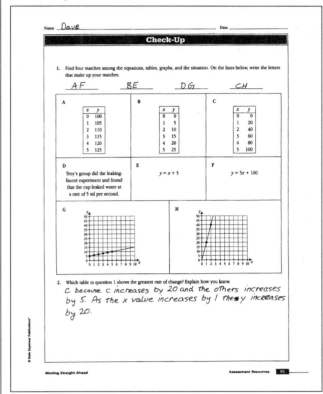

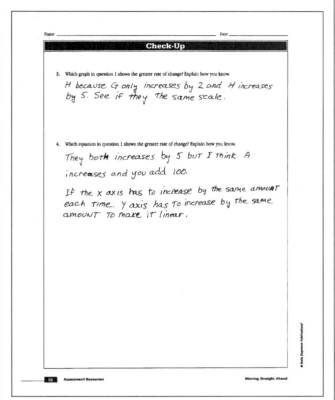

Teacher's Comments on Dave's Check-Up

Dave earned 4 points for his work on this check-up. He only had two of the pairs of representations in question 1 correct, so he received 2 of the 3 points for that question. Dave earned 2 points for question 2 but 0 points for questions 3 and 4. For question 3, his statement about the increments is not reasonable. For question 4, he implies that the two equations are the same because they both are increasing by 5. He is confused about how a constant of 5 and a coefficient of 5 affect the rate of change.

Although Dave is struggling with the ideas in this check-up, his and other students' errors and mis-conceptions helped me to think about what I need to re-address and focus on in future lessons. I will talk to Dave about his explanation in question 3 because I'm not sure what he is referring to. I need to know more about what he is thinking so I can find ways to address his misconception.

Scoring Quiz B

In this class, students worked on this assessment in pairs. They were allowed to turn their paper in once, get feedback from the teacher, revise their work, and resubmit it for a grade.

Point Rubric

A total of 24 points was assigned by this teacher to this assessment task.

14 points for questions 1–5

- 2 points, one for each correct equation
- 1 point for correct distances if supporting work is given
- 1 point for correctly identifying the intersection and supporting the answer
- 5 points for the y-intercept: 1 point for each correct y-intercept and 1 point for each reasonable explanation of how to find the y-intercept in each representation
- 5 points for the slope: 1 point for each correct slope and 1 point for each reasonable explanation of how to find the slope in each representation

4 points for questions 6–9

- 1 point for each correctly solved equation

2 points for question 10

- 2 points for a complete explanation, 1 point for a partial explanation

2 points for question 11

- 2 points for a complete explanation, 1 point for a partial explanation

2 points for question 12

- 1 point for identifying the slope
- 1 point for identifying the y-intercept

Grading Scale

Points	Grade
21 to 24	A
18 to 20	B
15 to 17	C
12 to 14	D

Sample 1

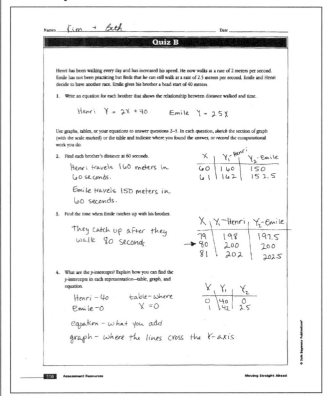

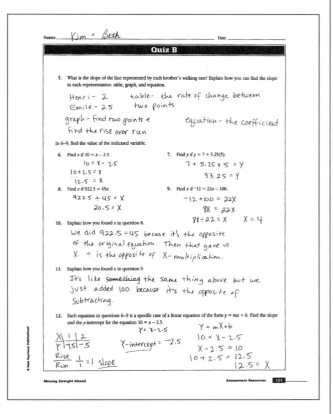

Teacher's Comments on Beth and Kim's Quiz B

Beth and Kim earned 21.5 of the 24 points given for this quiz. They correctly answered questions 1–3 and received all the points assigned. For question 4 they received only half credit for their explanation on how to find the *y*-intercept from an equation. Their statement "what you add" is not complete or clear enough for full credit. They needed to clarify what they were talking about. They received 4.5 points for this part. For question 5 they did not receive any credit for their explanation on how to find the slope from a table representation. They said, "the rate of change between two points" but did not explain how to find that rate of change in a table. A total of 4 points was earned for this part.

For questions 6–9, Beth and Kim found the correct value for each variable. Their work suggests that they solved each equation by using inverse operations. The students received full credit for their explanation for question 10 but only half credit for their explanation for question 11. They needed to explain that they had to first add 100 before they could divide by 22.

Beth and Kim's work for question 12 makes it clearer how they found the slope for the given equation. Their work even suggests that they may have learned something from doing this problem. By constructing and finding a couple of values for a table related to the equation, they found the rise

and run between two points and thus the slope. It appears that they could not just use the equation to give slope. The question I have as a teacher is, after finding slope as they did, do the students now see how they could have found slope for the given equation?

On the whole, Beth and Kim appear to be making reasonable sense of the mathematics we have studied in this unit to date. They both need to work harder on explaining what they know. They are making too many assumptions about how much a teacher should read into their answers. Although I did not take away many points for their lack of clarity and completeness in their explanations, I did express my concern about this issue in a note to them. These two students were not the only ones with this problem. When I returned the quizzes, I talked about what it meant to "explain" your actions and your thinking. I showed students' work in which the answers were more complete. I need to think more about this. On the whole, at this point in the year and into the Connected Mathematics curriculum, I expect my students to give better explanations than what these students have done.

Sample 2

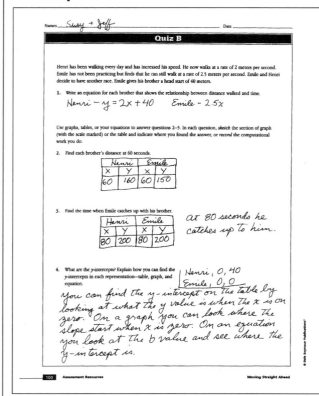

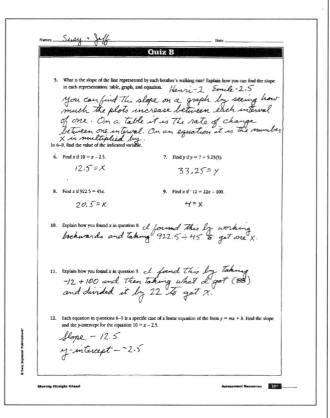

Teacher's Comments on Susy and Jeff's Quiz B

Susy and Jeff earned 20.5 points for their work on this quiz. These students earned 1.5 points for question 1. The equation given for Emile is really an expression and not an equation, so half a point was subtracted. This should not have been a difficult equation for students to write. Emile's walking rate did not change in this problem compared to his rate in the investigation. The correct equation could have been referenced from the student edition. Therefore, I expect students to have a correct equation. For questions 2–4, Susy and Jeff received full credit. Their explanation for how to find the y-intercept in a graph is of some concern to me because they say "look where the slope start(s)." However, because they add to that "when x is zero," I felt that they understood how they could find the y-intercept. For question 5, Susy and Jeff received only 3 of the 5 points. They did not receive points for their explanations on how to find the slope in a graph and a table. Neither explanation was clear enough for the reader to feel confident that the students understood and could find slope in these two representations.

For questions 6–9, Susy and Jeff received full credit. They did not show how they found their solutions but as that was not asked for in the problem, they were not marked down. For questions 10 and 11, Susy and Jeff received full credit because their descriptions would give a correct answer. For question 12, Susy and Jeff received 1 point for the correct y-intercept.

Susy and Jeff seem to have a pretty good understanding of the mathematics in this unit at this point. Nothing in their paper suggests that I should not move on in the unit. I am not sure that these two and some of my other students *understand* why they are doing the adding, subtracting, and dividing of numbers that they say they do to find unknown variables. I would like to know how my students are thinking about this.

Blackline Masters

In this experiment, you will simulate a leaking faucet and collect data about the volume of water lost at 5-second intervals. You will then use the patterns in your results to predict how much water is wasted when a faucet leaks for one month.

Equipment: a paper cup, water, a sharp object (such as a paper clip or a small nail), a clear measuring container, and a watch or clock with a second hand

Directions: You will need to figure out how to divide the work among the members of your group.

1. Make a table with columns for recording time and amount of water lost. Fill in the time column with values from 0 seconds to 60 seconds in 5-second intervals (that is, 5, 10, 15, and so on).

2. Use the sharp object to punch a small hole in the bottom of the cup. Cover the hole with your finger.

3. Fill the paper cup with water.

4. Hold the paper cup over the measuring container.

5. When you are ready to begin timing, uncover the hole so that the water drips into the measuring container.

6. In a table, record the amount of water in the measuring container at 5-second intervals, up to a total time of 60 seconds.

In this experiment, you will investigate how the height from which a ball is dropped is related to the height it bounces.

Equipment: a meterstick and a ball that bounces

Directions: You will need to figure out how to divide up the work among the members of your group.

1. Make a table with columns for recording drop height and bounce height.

2. Hold the meterstick perpendicular to a flat surface, such as an uncarpeted floor, a table, or a desk.

3. Choose and record a height on the meterstick as the height from which you will drop the ball. Hold the ball at this height.

4. *Drop* the ball, and record the height of the first bounce. (You may have to do this several times before you feel confident you can make a good estimate of the bounce height.)

5. Repeat this for several different drop heights.

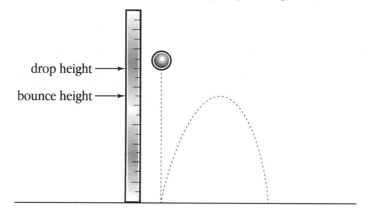

A. Make a coordinate graph of the data you collected.

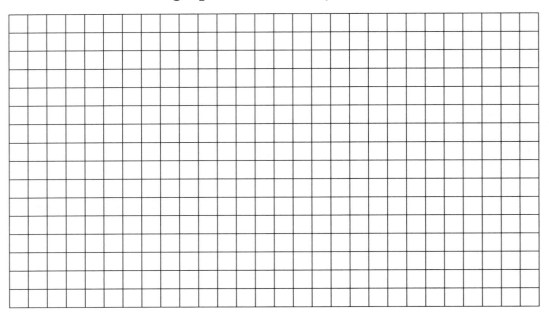

B. What variables did you investigate in this experiment? Describe the relationship between the variables.

C. If a faucet dripped at the same rate as your cup does, how much water would be wasted in 2 minutes? In 2.5 minutes? In 3 minutes and 15 seconds? Explain how you made your predictions. Did you use the table, the graph, or some other method? What clues in the data helped you?

A. Make a coordinate graph of the data you collected.

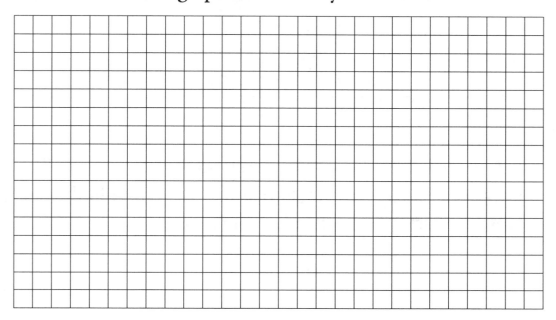

B. What variables did you investigate in this experiment? Describe the relationship between the variables.

C. Predict the bounce height for a drop height of 2 meters. Explain how you made your prediction.

D. Predict the drop height needed for a bounce height of 2 meters. Explain how you made your prediction.

E. What bounce height would you expect for a drop height of 0 centimeters? Where would this be on the graph?

Name	Walking rate
Terry	1 meter per second
Jade	2 meters per second
Jerome	2.5 meters per second

A. If Terry, Jade, and Jerome leave school together and walk toward the frozen yogurt shop at the rates given in the table, how far apart will they be after 1 minute?

B. If the yogurt shop is 750 meters from school, how long will it take each student to walk there?

C. When Jerome arrives at the yogurt shop, how far away will Terry be?

A. Use the walking rates given in Problem 2.1 to make a table showing the distance walked by each student after different numbers of seconds. How does the walking rate affect the data in the table?

Time	Distance (meters)		
(seconds)	Terry	Jade	Jerome
0	0	0	0
1	1	2	2.5
2			
3			

B. Graph the time and distance data for the three students on the same coordinate axes. How does the walking rate affect the graphs?

C. For each student, write an equation that gives the relationship between the time and the distance walked. Let *d* represent the distance in meters and *t* represent the time in seconds. How does the walking rate affect the equations?

Leanne: $1 per mile   *Gilberto:* $2 per mile
Alana: $5 plus 50¢ per mile

A. 1. Make a table showing the amount of money a sponsor would owe under each pledge plan if a student walked distances between 0 and 10 miles.

Distance (miles)	Money owed		
	Leanne	Gilberto	Alana
0			
1			
2			
3			
4			
5			
6			
7			
8			
9			
10			

2. Graph the three pledge plans on the same coordinate axes. Use a different color for each plan.

3. For each pledge plan, write an equation that can be used to calculate the amount of money a sponsor owes, given the total distance the student walks.

B. What effect does increasing the amount pledged per mile have on the table? On the graph? On the equation?

C. If a student walks 8 miles in the walkathon, how much would a sponsor owe under each pledge plan? Explain how you got your answer.

D. For a sponsor to owe a student $10, how many miles would the student have to walk under each pledge plan? Explain how you got your answer.

E. Alana suggested that each sponsor make a $5 donation and then pledge 50¢ per mile. How is this fixed $5 donation represented in the table? In the graph? In the equation?

In Mr. Goldberg's gym class, Emile finds out that his walking rate is 2.5 meters per second. When he gets home from school, he times his little brother Henri, as Henri walks 100 meters. He figures out that Henri's walking rate is 1 meter per second.

Emile knows his brother would enjoy winning the race, but he does not want to make the race so short that it is obvious his brother will win.

What would be a good distance to make the race so that Henri will win in a close race? Describe your strategy, and give evidence to support your answer.

A. 1. Make a table showing the distance each brother is from the starting line at several times during the first 40 seconds.

Time (seconds)	Henri's distance from starting line (meters)	Emile's distance from starting line (meters)

2. On the same set of axes, graph the time and the distance from the starting line for both brothers.

3. Write an equation for each brother showing the relationship between the time and the distance from the starting line.

B. How far from the starting line will Emile overtake Henri? Explain how you can use the table and the graph to answer this question.

C. After how many seconds will Emile overtake Henri? Explain how you can use the table and the graph to answer this question.

Look at the table and the graph you made for Alana's pledge plan.

A. The point (14, 12) is on the graph of Alana's plan. Write a question you could answer by locating this point.

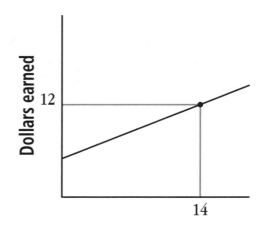

B. How can you use the equation for Alana's plan to check the answer to the question you wrote in part A?

C. **1.** For a sponsor to owe a student $17 under Alana's pledge plan, how many miles would the student have to walk?

2. Was the graph or the equation more helpful in answering part 1?

In A–D, consider the following suggested pledge plans. In each equation, y is the amount owed in dollars, and x is the number of miles walked.

i. $y = 3x$ ii. $y = {}^-2x$ iii. $y = 5x - 3$

iv. $y = {}^-x + 6$ v. $y = 2$

A. What does each pledge plan mean?

B. Without using your graphing calculator, make a table of x and y values for each pledge plan. Use the x values 1, 2, 3, 4, and 5. Use your tables to help you decide which plans are reasonable. Explain how you made your decisions.

C. Graph each pledge plan with a graphing calculator. Use a window that shows the graph clearly. Make a sketch of the graph you see.

D. For each pledge plan, tell whether the *y* values increase, decrease, or stay the same as the *x* values increase. How can you tell from the graph? From the table? From the equation?

In A–D, consider the following equations.

i. $y = 3x$ ii. $y = {}^{-}2x$ iii. $y = 5x - 3$

iv. $y = {}^{-}x + 6$ v. $y = 2$

A. 1. Which equation has a graph you can trace to find the value of x that makes $^{-}8 = 5x - 3$ a true statement?

    2. Use your graphing calculator to find the value of x. We call this value the *solution* to the equation $^{-}8 = 5x - 3$.

B. 1. Which equation has a table you can use to find the value of x that makes $6.8 = {}^{-}2x$ a true statement?

    2. Make a table with your graphing calculator, and find the value of x. Copy the part of the table you used to find the solution.

C. Find solutions for the equations $^-8 = 5x - 3$ and $6.8 = ^-2x$ by reasoning about what the equations mean rather than by using graphs or tables. Explain how you found the solutions.

D. 1. How does finding the solution to $^-8 = 5x - 3$ help you find a coordinate pair that fits the equation $y = 5x - 3$?

    2. Find three other coordinate pairs that fit the equation $y = 5x - 3$. How can you prove your coordinate pairs fit the equation?

Suppose your class is planning a skating party to celebrate the end of the school year. Your committee is in charge of finding a place to rent in-line skates for a reasonable price. You get quotes from two companies:

Roll-Away Skates charges $5 per person.

Wheelie's Skates and Stuff charges $100 plus $3 per person.

Which company should you choose if you want to keep the cost to a minimum? Explain how you made your choice.

The Unlimited Store allows any customer who buys merchandise costing over $30 to pay on an installment plan. The customer pays $30 down and then pays $15 a month until the item is paid for.

Suppose you buy a $195 CD-ROM drive from the Unlimited Store on an installment plan. How many months will it take you to pay for the drive? Describe how you found your answer.

Thinking	Manipulating the Symbols
	195 = 30 + 15N
"I want to buy a CD-ROM drive that costs \$195. To pay for the drive on the installment plan, I must pay \$30 down and \$15 a month."	$195 = 30 + 15N$
"After I pay the \$30 down payment, I can subtract this from the cost. To keep the sides of the equation equal, I must subtract 30 from both sides."	$95 - 30 = 30 - 30 + 15N$
"I now owe \$165, which I will pay in monthly installments of \$15."	$165 = 15N$
"I need to separate \$165 into payments of \$15. This means I need to divide it by 15. To keep the sides of the equation equal, I must divide both sides by 15."	$\frac{165}{15} = \frac{15N}{15}$
"There are 11 groups of \$15 in \$165, so it will take 11 months."	$11 = N$

The cost of the stove has to balance $30 + 15N$.

In symbols, $30 + 15N = 305$.

If I subtract \$30 from the left side, . . .

. . . I need to balance this by subtracting \$30 from the right side.

In symbols, $30 - 30 + 15N = 305 - 30$.

But I want to know what N is, not $15N$. I want to know how many groups of 15 are in 275. Since $275 \div 15 = 18\frac{1}{3}$, there are $18\frac{1}{3}$ groups of 15 in 275.

Dividing both sides by 15 shows that one N matches with $18\frac{1}{3}$, so I know what N balances!

In symbols, $\frac{15N}{15} = \frac{275}{15}$ or $N = 18\frac{1}{3}$.

Karen wants to buy a stove from the Unlimited Store on an installment plan. The stove costs $305.

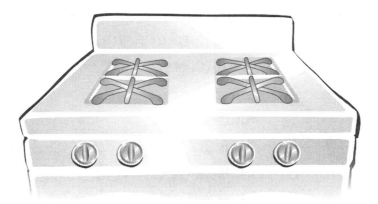

A. Write an equation you could solve to find the number of months it will take Karen to pay for the stove.

B. Solve your equation by using the symbolic method. How many months will it take Karen to pay for the stove?

The table gives equations for the relationships between the length of each bone and the height for males and females. F represents the length of the femur, T the length of the tibia, H the length of the humerus, R the length of the radius, and h the person's height. All measurements are in centimeters.

Bone	Male	Female
Femur	$h = 69.089 + 2.238F$	$h = 61.412 + 2.317F$
Tibia	$h = 81.688 + 2.392T$	$h = 72.572 + 2.533T$
Humerus	$h = 73.570 + 2.970H$	$h = 64.977 + 3.144H$
Radius	$h = 80.405 + 3.650R$	$h = 73.502 + 3.876R$

Source: George Knill. "Mathematics in Forensic Science." *Mathematics Teacher* (February 1981): 31–32.

A. How tall is a female if her femur is 46.2 centimeters long?

B. How tall is a male if his tibia is 50.1 centimeters long?

C. If a woman is 152 centimeters (about 5 feet) tall, how long is her femur? Her tibia? Her humerus? Her radius?

D. If a man is 183 centimeters (about 6 feet) tall, how long is his femur? His tibia? His humerus? His radius?

Carpenters have developed guidelines to ensure the stairs they build are relatively easy for a person to climb. In some states, carpenters work with these guidelines:

- The ratio of rise to run for each step should be between 0.45 and 0.60.
- The rise plus the run for each step should be between 17 and 17.5 inches.

Determine the steepness of a set of stairs. To calculate the steepness you will need to measure the rise and the run of a step. Measure at least two steps in the set of stairs you choose. Make a sketch of the stairs, and label it with the measurements you found.

How do the stairs you measured compare with the guidelines above?

Do parts A–D for each equation below.

i. $y = 2x$ ii. $y = {}^-3x$ iii. $y = 5 + 2x$

iv. $y = \frac{1}{2}x + 2$ v. $y = 2 - 3x$

A. Make a table of x and y values for the equation. Use the x values $^-3, {}^-2, {}^-1, 0, 1, 2, 3,$ and 4.

B. On grid paper, make a graph of the equation.

C. Choose two points on the line, and compute the ratio of the vertical change to the horizontal change from one point to the other. Would you get the same ratio if you had chosen two different points? Choose two different points, and check your answer.

D. The ratio you computed in part C is the slope of the line. How is the slope of the line related to the table of values for the line? How is it related to the equation for the line?

Do parts A–E for each pair of points below.

i. (2, 6) and (0, 4)   ii. (2, 3) and (4, 6)   iii. (0, 3) and (1, 4)
iv. (⁻1, 3) and (1, 0)   v. (1, 4) and (3, 4)   vi. (4, 1) and (⁻4, 2)

A. Plot the points on a coordinate grid, and draw the line that passes through them.

B. Do the y values for points on the line increase, decrease, or stay the same as the x values increase?

C. Find the slope of the line.

D. Mark and label at least three other points on the line, and record the x and y values for the points in an organized table. Does the pattern in your table confirm the slope you found in part B?

E. Use the graph or the table to find the y-intercept of the line.

A. Alphonso tells Maria he will save the same amount from his allowance each week. He says that after five weeks he will have a total of $175 and after eight weeks he will have $190. How much money is Alphonso planning to save each week?

B. How much money did Alphonso's grandfather give him for his birthday?

Two important reference points for temperature are the boiling point and the freezing point of water. Water freezes at 0°C, or 32°F. Water boils at 100°C, or 212°F.

0°C, or 32°F　　　　　　　100°C, or 212°F

Use this information to write an equation for the relationship between Fahrenheit degrees and Celsius degrees.

A. Since the relationship represented in the table below is linear, its equation can be written in the form $y = mx + b$. You know the slope is 2.4, so the equation becomes $y = 2.4x + b$. Now you need to find the value of b, the y-intercept.

x	46	47.1	48.1	49	50.1
y	31.5	34.14	36.54	38.7	41.34

To find b, pick a pair of x and y values from the table, and substitute them into the equation

$$\boxed{} = 2.4\,\boxed{} + b$$

What value must b have? Substitute this value into $y = 2.4x + b$ to complete the equation.

B. Use your equation from part A to predict the antler length for a skull length of 55 centimeters.

C. For each Irish elk represented in the table, the antler length is shorter than the skull length. However, the Irish elk skeleton shown on page 82 has antlers much longer than its skull. Can you explain how the skull and antler data for this elk could fit the equation you wrote?

Dear Family,

The next unit in your child's course of study in mathematics class this year is *Moving Straight Ahead.* In this unit, students are developing skills in areas that are traditionally known as algebra. This unit introduces them to situations that can be modeled with linear functions and graphed with straight lines.

We have structured this unit so that students are exposed to linear and nonlinear situations in a variety of forms: tables, graphs, and algebraic equations. Students are encouraged to move freely from one form to another and to use the different forms in various situations. They are introduced to several other important algebraic terms and concepts—like x- and y-intercepts and the slope of a line—that will be built on in later units. Students encounter these and other ideas in real-world situations that help them understand the concepts in ways that make sense to them.

Here are some strategies for helping your child work with the ideas in this unit:

- Ask your child to describe some real-world situations in which linear functions are used and to explain how the situation can be described using a table, a graph, and an equation. Here are some examples:

  — Phone charges that increase at a constant rate based on the length of the call

  — The distance traveled in a vehicle moving at a constant speed

  — The amount of water in a sink that is draining at a constant rate

- Look at your child's mathematics notebook. You may want to read some of the explanations that have been written and, if they aren't clear, talk with your child about why you think they may need more explanation.

- Encourage your child's efforts in completing homework assignments, and help make sure your child understands the work that has been done.

As always, if you have any questions or concerns about this unit or your child's progress in the class, please feel free to call. We are interested in your child's success in mathematics.

Sincerely,

Estimada familia,

La próxima unidad del programa de matemáticas de su hijo o hija para este curso se llama *Moving Straight Ahead* (Sigamos adelante). En ella los alumnos continuarán perfeccionando sus destrezas en lo que tradicionalmente se conoce como el álgebra. Conocerán situaciones que pueden representarse mediante funciones lineales y cuya gráfica es una línea recta.

Esta unidad ha sido estructurada de manera tal que los alumnos examinarán situaciones lineales y no lineales en una diversidad de formas: tablas, gráficas y ecuaciones algebraicas. Se les anima a pasar de una forma a otra y a usar las distintas formas en una variedad de situaciones. Aprenderán también otros nuevos e importantes términos y conceptos algebraicos como, por ejemplo, las intercepciones en x e y y la pendiente de una recta, los cuales volverán a tratarse con más profundidad en unidades posteriores. Es más, los alumnos verán estas y otras ideas en situaciones del mundo real, lo cual les ayudará a comprender su aplicación en un contexto práctico.

He aquí algunas estrategias que ustedes pueden emplear para ayudar a su hijo o hija con las ideas de esta unidad:

■ Pídanle que describa algunas situaciones del mundo real en las que se utilicen funciones lineales y que les explique cómo describir dichas situaciones mediante una tabla, una gráfica y una ecuación. Aparecen a continuación algunos ejemplos:

— El importe de las llamadas telefónicas cuando éste aumenta siguiendo una tasa constante según la duración de la llamada

— La distancia recorrida por un vehículo que se desplaza a una velocidad constante

— La cantidad de agua que a un ritmo constante desagua un lavabo

■ Repasen su cuaderno de matemáticas. Es recomendable que lean algunas de sus explicaciones y, de resultar poco claras, que comenten con su hijo o hija las razones a favor de ampliar dichas explicaciones.

■ Anímenle a esforzarse para que complete toda la tarea y asegúrense de que comprende el trabajo que ha hecho.

Y como de costumbre, si ustedes necesitan más detalles o aclaraciones respecto a la unidad o sobre los progresos de su hijo o hija en esta clase, no duden en llamarnos. Nos interesa que su hijo o hija avance en el estudio de las matemáticas.

Atentamente,

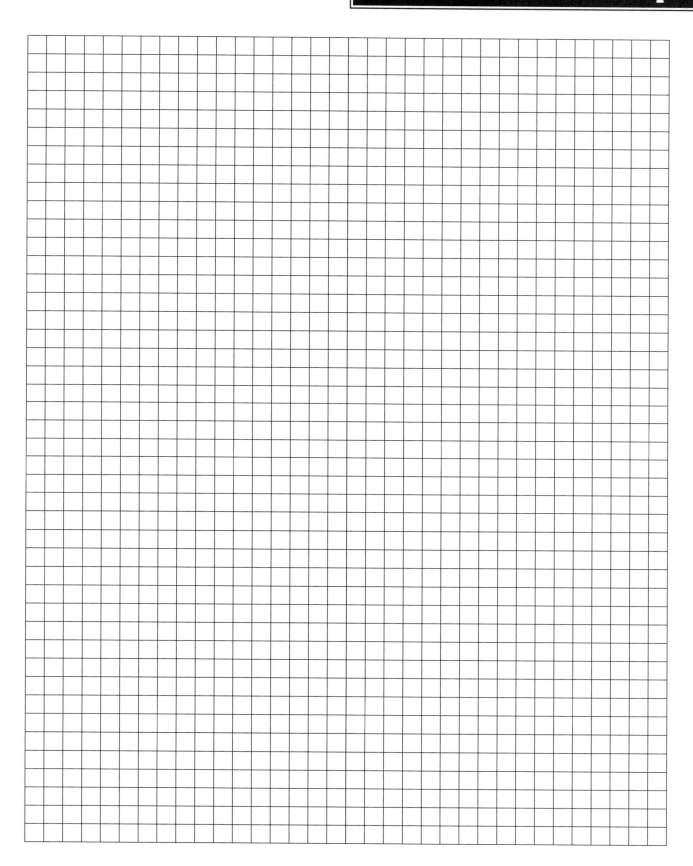

Centimeter Grid Paper

Additional Practice

Investigation 1

Use these problems for additional practice after Investigation 1.

1. Isaac and Dominique counted the number of students who passed through the cafeteria line. They recorded a new total each minute for 8 minutes. They organized the data in this table.

Time (minutes)	1	2	3	4	5	6	7	8
Number of students	9	21	30	39	48	59	70	81

   a. Make a graph of the data with time on the *x*-axis and the number of students on the *y*-axis.

   b. Predict how much time it would take for 55 students to pass through the cafeteria line.

   c. How many students would you expect to buy lunches in a 10-minute period?

   d. Predict how many students could buy lunches over a 30-minute period.

2. Manoj put sand into a clear graduated cylinder with a small opening in the bottom. He let the sand run out of the opening, and he measured the height of the sand remaining in the cylinder at 10-second intervals. The height of the sand in the cylinder was 80 mm when he began his experiment.

Time (seconds)	0	10	20	30	40	50
Height of sand (mm)	80	65	49	36	21	5

   a. Make a graph of the data.

   b. Predict the height of sand in the cylinder after 25 seconds had elapsed.

   c. Predict the time that had elapsed when the height of sand was 72 mm.

   d. How long do you think it took for all the sand to run out of the cylinder? Explain your reasoning.

   e. How confident are you in the predictions you made? Explain.

Investigation 2

Use these problems for additional practice after Investigation 2.

In 1–3, refer to this table, which Francine, Geraldo, and Jennifer made during a bicycling trip. It shows the distance each person traveled during the first four hours of their trip. The table shows the distance covered while the students were actually biking. (Time is not counted when they stop to rest, eat, etc.)

Cycling time (hours)	Distance (miles)		
	Francine	Geraldo	Jennifer
0	0	0	0
1	4.5	6	7.5
2	9	12	15
3	13.5	18	22.5
4	18	24	30

1. **a.** How fast did each person travel for the first four hours? Explain how you arrived at your answer.

   b. Assume that each person continued at this rate. Find the distance each person traveled in 6 hours.

2. **a.** Graph the time and distance for all three people on the same coordinate axes.

   b. Use the graphs to find the distance each person traveled in 2.5 hours.

   c. Use the graphs to find the time it took each person to travel 70 miles.

   d. How does the rate at which each person rides affect the graphs?

3. **a.** For each rider, write an equation you can use to calculate the distance traveled after a given number of hours.

   b. Describe how you could use your equations to calculate the distance each person traveled in 2.5 hours.

   c. How does each person's biking rate show up in the equation?

4. Stilton was also on the bike trip. The distance he traveled after t hours is represented by $d = 7.25t$.

   a. At what rate of speed is Stilton traveling?

   b. If you were to put the graph of Stilton's distance and time on the same set of axes as the graphs for Francine, Geraldo, and Jennifer, how would it compare to the other three graphs?

5. Each set of (x, y) coordinates below is generated by a linear rule. For each set of coordinates, write an equation to describe the rule.

   a. $(^-1, ^-7)$, $(0, ^-3)$, $(1, 1)$, $(2, 5)$, $(4, 13)$, $(5, 17)$

   b. $(^-2, 19)$, $(^-1, 14)$, $(0, 9)$, $(2, ^-1)$ $(4, ^-11)$, $(6, ^-21)$

   c. $(^-2, ^-1)$, $(0, 3)$, $(1, 5)$, $(3, 9)$, $(5, 13)$, $(6, 15)$

In 6–8, use the graph below to answer the questions.

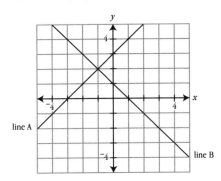

6. Make a table showing the coordinates of four points located on line A. What is the equation for line A?

7. Make a table showing the coordinates of four points located on line B. What is the equation for line B?

8. Is there is a point with (*x*, *y*) coordinates that satisfies both the equation for line A and the equation for line B? Explain your reasoning.

9. Martin used some rules to generate the following tables:

i.

x	*y*
⁻1	6
0	8
1	10
2	12
3	14

ii.

x	*y*
0	5
3	5
6	5
9	5
12	5

iii.

x	*y*
⁻2	⁻5
⁻1	⁻4.5
0	⁻4
3	⁻2.5
4	⁻2
5	⁻1.5

iv.

x	*y*
⁻1	0.5
0	0
1	0.5
2	2
3	4.5
4	8
5	12.5

a. Make a graph of the data in each table. Show the graphs on the same coordinate axes.

b. Which sets of data represent a linear relationships? How do you know?

10. The equations below represent the costs to print brochures at three different printers.

a. For which equation does the point (20, 60) lie on the graph? Explain.

  i. $C = 15 + 2.50N$ ii. $C = 50 + 1.75N$ iii. $C = 30 + 1.50N$

b. For each equation, give the coordinates of a point on the graph of the equation.

11. The equations below represent the distances in meters traveled after *t* seconds by three cyclists.

a. For which equation does the point (10, 74) lie on the graph? Explain.

  i. $D = 2.4t + 32$ ii. $D = 4.2t + 32$ iii. $D = 6t + 32$

b. For each equation, give the coordinates of a point on the graph of the equation.

Investigation 3

Use these problems for additional practice after Investigation 3.

1. Do parts a–e for each equation below.

   i. $y = 2.5x$ **ii.** $y = {}^-2x + 7$ **iii.** $y = {}^-4x - 8$ **iv.** $y = 3x - 3$

   a. Graph the equation on your calculator, and make a sketch of the line you see.

   b. What ranges of x and y values did you use for your window?

   c. Do the y values increase, decrease, or stay the same as the x values increase?

   d. Give the y-intercept.

   e. List the coordinates of three points on the line.

2. The volleyball team decided to raise money for an end-of-season party by selling school buttons. The costs and the revenue of selling the buttons are shown on the graph below.

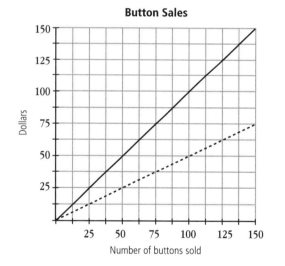

   a. If the team sells 50 buttons, what will be their cost? What will be the revenue?

   b. If the team sells 50 buttons, how much profit will they make? (Remember that the profit is the revenue minus the cost.)

   c. If the team sells 100 buttons, how much profit will they make?

3. a. Graph the equation $y = 5x + 7$ on your calculator. Use the graph to find the missing coordinates for these points on the graph: (2, ?), (?, 52), and (2.9, ?).

   b. Graph the equation $y = 1.5x - 4$ on your calculator. Use the graph to find the missing coordinates for these points on the graph: (10, ?) and (?, 32).

   c. Graph the equation $y = 6.25 - 3x$ on your calculator. Use the graph to find the missing coordinates for these points on the graph: (5, ?) and ($^-2.75$, ?).

4. Use the graph below to answer a–d.

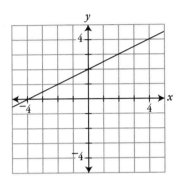

a. List the coordinates of three points on the line.

b. Which equation below is the equation of the line?

   i. $y = x + 4$ ii. $y = 0.5x + 2$ iii. $y = 0.5x - 5$ iv. $y = 4 - 0.5x$

c. Does the point (56, 35) lie on the line? Explain your reasoning.

d. Does the point (⁻20, ⁻8) lie on line? Explain your reasoning.

5. Do parts a and b for each pair of equations below.

   i. $y = \frac{-12}{5}x - 6$ ii. $y = x - 3$ iii. $y = x + 9$ iv. $y = 2x - 6$

   $y = 4x + 14$ $y = ^{-}1.5x + 12$ $y = 7 - 3x$ $y = ^{-}2$

a. Graph the two equations on the same axes. Use window settings that allow you to see the points where the graphs intersect. What ranges of x and y values did you use for your window?

b. Find the point of intersection of the graphs.

c. Test the point of intersection you found by substituting its coordinates into the equations. Did the points fit the equation exactly? Explain why or why not.

© Dale Seymour Publications®

Investigation 4

Use these problems for additional practice after Investigation 4.

1. **a.** Find r if $2r + 10 = 22$.   **b.** Find x if $4.5x = 45$.

    c. Find z if $3z - 19 = 173$.   **d.** Find w if $67.1 = 29.7 - 0.2w$.

2. Betty is thinking of two consecutive integers whose sum is 41. Let x represent the smaller unknown integer.

    a. How could you represent the larger unknown integer in terms of x?

    b. Write an equation showing that the sum of the two unknown integers is 41.

    c. Solve your equation. What integers Betty is thinking of?

3. Find the number described in each problem by writing and solving an equation.

    a. If Sarah subtracts five times her number from 24, she gets 4. What is Sarah's number?

    b. Twice Bill's number added to 17 is 7. What is Bill's number?

    c. The sum of 4 times a number and 14 is 16. What is the number?

    d. If Susan subtracts 11 from one fourth of her number she gets 11. What is Susan's number?

4. The school drama club is performing its summer play at the community theater. Props for the play cost $250, and the theater is charging the drama club $1.25 for each ticket sold. So, the total cost, C, for the drama club to put on the play is $C = 1.25N + 250$, where N is the number of tickets sold. Customers pay $4 for each ticket, so the total amount collected from ticket sales is $T = 4N$.

    a. What is the cost if 213 tickets are sold?

    b. How much are the total ticket sales if 213 tickets are sold?

    c. What is the drama club's profit or loss if 213 tickets are sold?

    d. If the total ticket sales are $780, how many people attended the play?

    e. What is the cost of putting on the play for the number of people you found in d?

    f. How many tickets does the drama club need to sell to break even?

    g. The drama club would like to earn a profit of $500 from the play. How many tickets need to be sold for the club to meet this goal?

Investigation 5

Use these problems for additional practice after Investigation 5.

1. Find the slope and *y*-intercept of the line represented by each equation.

   a. $y = 2x - 10$ b. $y = 4x + 3$ c. $y = 4x - 4.5$

   d. $y = 2.6x$ e. $y = 7x + 1$

2. Each table in i–v below represents a linear relationship. Do parts a–c for each table.

   a. Find the slope of the line that represents the relationship.

   b. Find the *y*-intercept for the graph of the relationship.

   c. Determine which of the following equations represents the relationship:

   $y = 3 - 4x$ $y = x + 6$ $y = 4x - 3$ $y = 3x - 1.5$ $y = 2.5x$

i.

x	y
0	0
1	2.5
2	5
3	7.5
4	10

ii.

x	y
0	6
1	7
2	8
3	9
4	10

iii.

x	y
0	⁻1.5
1	1.5
2	4.5
3	7.5
4	10.5

iv.

x	y
0	3
1	⁻1
2	⁻5
3	⁻9
4	⁻13

v.

x	y
1	1
2	5
3	9
4	13
5	17

3. For each of the lines below, find the slope, and write an equation that represents the line.

   a.
   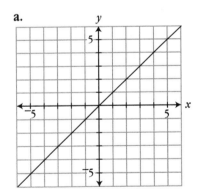

   b.
   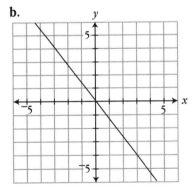

   c.
   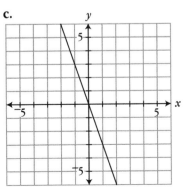

4. Do parts a–d for each pair of points below.

   i. (0, 0) and (⁻3, ⁻3)   **ii.** (1, ⁻1) and (⁻3, 3)

   a. Plot the points on a coordinate grid, and draw the line through the points.

   b. Find the slope of the line through the points.

   c. Estimate the *y*-intercept from the graph.

   d. Using your answers from parts a and b, write an equation for the line through the points.

5. On Saturdays, Jim likes to go to the mall to play video games or pinball. Round-trip bus fare to and from the mall is $1.80. Jim spends $0.50 for each video or pinball game.

   a. Write an equation for the amount of money, *M*, it costs Jim to go to the mall and play *n* video or pinball games.

   b. What is the slope of the line your equation represents? What does the slope tell you about this situation?

   c. What is the *y*-intercept of the line? What does the *y*-intercept tell you about the situation?

   d. How much will it cost Jim to travel to the mall and play 8 video or pinball games?

   e. If Jim has $6.75, how many video or pinball games can he play at the mall?

6. Angie likes to take the bus to the Comic Shop downtown. Below is a graph showing the total cost (including bus fare and the cost of comics) for her to go to the Comic Shop to buy new comic books.

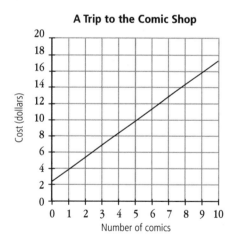

A Trip to the Comic Shop

   a. What is Angie's round-trip bus fare? Explain your reasoning.

   b. How much does a comic book cost at the Comic Shop? Explain your reasoning.

   c. Write an equation that shows how much money, *M*, it costs Angie to buy *n* comic books at the Comic Shop. What information did you use from the graph to write the equation?

7. Tonya is siphoning all the water from a full aquarium to clean it. The graph below shows the amount of water left in the aquarium as Tonya siphons the water.

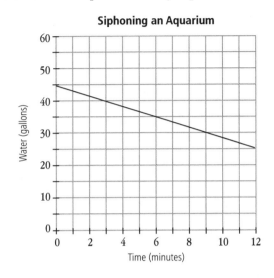

Siphoning an Aquarium

a. How much water was in the aquarium when it was full? Explain your reasoning.

b. How much water does the siphon remove from the aquarium in 1 minute? Explain your reasoning.

c. Write an equation that shows the amount of water, G, left in the aquarium after t minutes.

d. How many gallons of water are left in the aquarium after 10 minutes?

e. How long will it take the siphon to remove all of the water from the aquarium? Explain your reasoning.

Investigation 6

Use these problems for additional practice after Investigation 6.

1. In a–f, write an equation for the line that satisfies the given conditions.

   a. The slope is 7 and the *y*-intercept is ⁻2.

   b. The slope is 0 and the *y*-intercept is 9.18.

   c. The line passes through the points (3, 1) and (6, 4).

   d. The line passes through the points (⁻24, ⁻11) and (⁻8, ⁻3).

   e. The line passes through the points (⁻4.5, 2) and (6.3, 5.8).

   f. The slope is $\frac{-2}{3}$ and the line passes through the point (5, 0).

2. Write an equation for each of the four lines shown on the graph below.

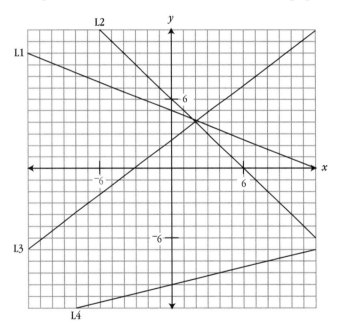

3. At Midtown Bowling Center, the cost to bowl four games is $8.40, and the cost to rent shoes is $1.15.

   a. Write an equation for the cost, *C*, for renting shoes and bowling *n* games.

   b. What is the *y*-intercept for your equation, and what does it represent?

   c. What is the slope of your equation, and what does the slope represent?

   d. What is the cost of renting shoes and bowling six games?

   e. Tony paid $7.45 for his games and shoe rental. How many games did Tony bowl?

Investigation 1

1. **a.**

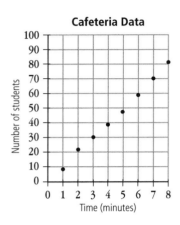

Cafeteria Data

   b. about 5.5 minutes

   c. about 100

   d. If 100 could buy lunches in 10 minutes, about $3 \times 100 = 300$ could buy lunches in 30 minutes.

2. **a.**

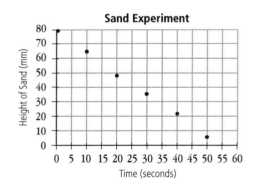

Sand Experiment

   b. about 42.5 mm

   c. about 5 seconds

   d. about 53 seconds; The sand runs out at a rate of about 1.5 mm per second, so it will take about 3 seconds for the last 5 mm to run out.

   e. Answers will vary.

Investigation 2

1. **a.** Francine: 4.5 mph; Geraldo: 6 mph; Jennifer: 7.5 mph; Divide the number of miles traveled in 4 hours by 4.

   b. Francine: 27 miles; Geraldo: 36 miles; Jennifer: 45 miles

2. **a.**

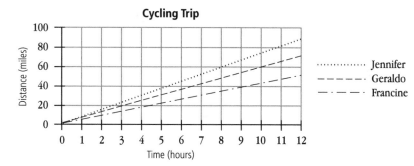

   b. Students' estimates should be close to the following values: Francine: 11.25 miles; Geraldo: 15 miles; Jennifer: 18.75 miles

   c. Students' estimates should be close to the following values: Francine: 15.6 hours; Geraldo: 11.7 hours; Jennifer: 9.3 hours

   d. The faster the cyclist, the steeper the graph.

3. **a.** Francine: $D = 4.5t$; Geraldo: $D = 6t$; Jennifer: $D = 7.5t$

   b. Substitute 2.5 for t in each equation.

   c. the number being multiplied by t

4. **a.** 7.25 miles per hour

   b. Stilton's graph would be steeper than Francine's and Geraldo's but less steep than Jennifer's.

5. **a.** $y = 4x - 3$ **b.** $y = 9 - 5x$ **c.** $y = 2x + 3$

6. $y = x + 3$

x	0	⁻1	⁻2	⁻3
y	3	2	1	0

7. $y = 1 - x$

x	0	1	2	3
y	1	0	⁻1	⁻2

8. Yes, the point is (⁻1, 2), which is where the two lines intersect on the graph. The point (⁻1, 2) is on both lines so it satisfies both equations.

9. a.

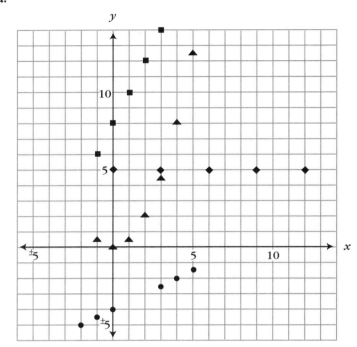

■	i
◆	ii
●	iii
▲	iv

b. Sets i, ii, and iii represent linear relationships. The graphs of these data sets are straight lines.

10. a. Equation iii because the point satisfies the equation: $60 = 30 + 1.5(20)$.

b. Answers will vary.

11. a. Equation ii because the point satisfies the equation: $74 = 4.2(10) + 32$.

b. Answers will vary.

Investigation 3

1. a. i.   a. ii.

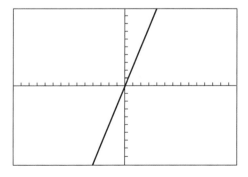   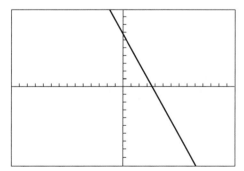

a. iii.

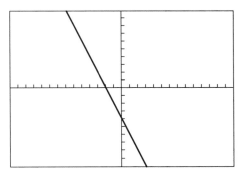

a. iv.

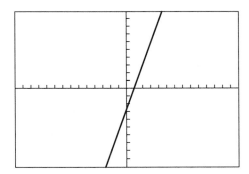

b. i.

```
WINDOW
  XMIN=-10
  XMAX=10
  XSCL=1
  YMIN=-10
  YMAX=10
  YSCL=1
```

b. ii.

```
WINDOW
  XMIN=-10
  XMAX=10
  XSCL=1
  YMIN=-10
  YMAX=10
  YSCL=1
```

b. iii.

```
WINDOW
  XMIN=-10
  XMAX=10
  XSCL=1
  YMIN=-20
  YMAX=20
  YSCL=2
```

b. iv.

```
WINDOW
  XMIN=-10
  XMAX=10
  XSCL=1
  YMIN=-10
  YMAX=10
  YSCL=1
```

c. **i.** increase

iii. decrease

ii. decrease

iv. increase

d. **i.** 0

iii. ⁻8

ii. 7

iv. ⁻3

e. **i.–iv.** Answers will vary

2. a. $25; $50

b. $25

c. $100 − $50 = $50

3. **a.** (2, 17), (9, 52), (2.9, 21.5)

   b. (10, 11), (24, 32)

   c. (5, ⁻8.75), (⁻2.75, 14.5)

4. **a.** Possible answer: (⁻4, 0), (0, 2), and (2, 3)

   b. ii. $y = 0.5x + 2$

   c. no; The x value 56 corresponds to the y value 30, not 35.

   d. yes; The x value ⁻20 does correspond to the y value ⁻8.

5. **a. i.**

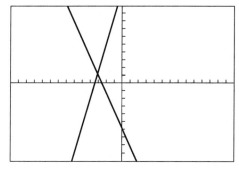

```
WINDOW
 XMIN=⁻10
 XMAX=10
 XSCL=1
 YMIN=⁻10
 YMAX=10
 YSCL=1
```

   ii.

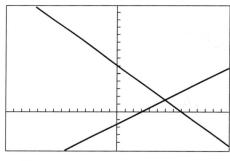

```
WINDOW
 XMIN=⁻10
 XMAX=10
 XSCL=1
 YMIN=⁻10
 YMAX=28
 YSCL=2
```

   iii.

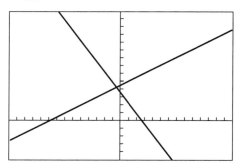

```
WINDOW
 XMIN=⁻10
 XMAX=10
 XSCL=1
 YMIN=⁻10
 YMAX=28
 YSCL=2
```

iv.

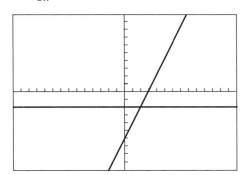

```
WINDOW
 XMIN=⁻10
 XMAX=10
 XSCL=1
 YMIN=⁻10
 YMAX=10
 YSCL=1
```

b. The exact answers are given here. If students found the intersection points by inspecting the graphs, their answers may not be exact.

   i. $(⁻3.125, 1.5)$ **ii.** $(6, 3)$ **iii.** $(⁻0.5, 8.5)$ **iv.** $(2, ⁻2)$

c. The values may not fit exactly because they may be estimates, but they should be close.

Investigation 4

1. **a.** $r = 6$ **b.** $x = 10$

   c. $z = 64$ **d.** $w = ⁻187$

2. **a.** $x + 1$

   b. $x + (x + 1) = 41$

   c. The equation in b is the same as $2x + 1 = 41$. Subtracting 1 from both sides gives us $2x = 40$, so $x = 20$ and $x + 1 = 21$.

3. **a.** $24 - 5x = 4; 4$ **b.** $2x + 17 = 7; x = ⁻5$

   c. $4x + 14 = 16; x = \frac{1}{2}$ **d.** $\frac{1}{4}x - 11 = 11; x = 88$

4. **a.** $516.25   **b.** $852   **c.** $335.75 profit

   d. 195   **e.** $493.75   **f.** 91

   g. 273

Investigation 5

1. **a.** slope is 2; y-intercept is $⁻10$

   b. slope is 4; y-intercept is 3

   c. slope is 4; y-intercept is $⁻4.5$

    d. slope is 2.6; *y*-intercept is 0

    e. slope is 7; *y*-intercept is 1

2. **i.** **a.** 2.5   **ii.** **a.** 1

      b. 0   **b.** 6

      c. $y = 2.5x$ **c.** $y = x + 6$

  iii. **a.** 3   **iv.** **a.** ⁻4

      b. ⁻1.5   **b.** 3

      c. $y = 3x - 1.5$ **c.** $y = 3 - 4x$

  v. **a.** 4

      b. ⁻3

      c. $y = 4x - 3$

3. **a.** slope is 1; $y = x$ **b.** slope is $\frac{^-4}{3}$; $y = \frac{^-4}{3}x$

    c. slope is ⁻3; $y = {^-3}x$

4. **a.**

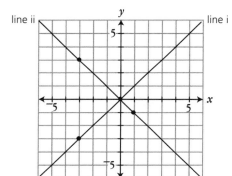

    b. **i.** slope = 1   **ii.** slope = ⁻1

    c. **i.** *y*-intercept = 0   **ii.** *y*-intercept = 0

    d. **i.** $y = x$ **ii.** $y = {^-x}$

5. **a.** $M = 0.5n + 1.80$

    b. 0.5 is slope; It is the cost of each game.

    c. 1.80 is the *y*-intercept; It is the bus fare.

    d. $5.80

    e. Jim can play 9 games, and he will have $0.45 left over.

6. **a.** $2.25; This is the intercept on the *y*-axis, which represents the cost if Angie buys 0 comics.

   b. $1.50; For each comic book purchased, the cost rises by $1.50.

   c. Using the slope and the y-intercept, the equation is $M = 1.5n + 2.25$.

7. **a.** 45 gallons; This is the y-intercept (the amount of water in the aquarium at $t = 0$).

   b. From the graph, the siphon removes 20 gallons in 12 minutes, or equivalently, $\frac{20}{12} = \frac{5}{3}$ gallons in 1 minute.

   c. $G = \frac{-5}{3}t + 45$

   d. Substitute 10 for t in the equation. You get $G = 28.33$ gallons of water left in the aquarium.

   e. Substitute 0 for G in the equation. You get $t = 27$ minutes.

Investigation 6

1. **a.** $y = 7x - 2$ **b.** $y = 9.18$ **c.** $y = x - 2$

   d. $y = 0.5x + 1$ **e.** $y = \frac{19}{54}x + \frac{43}{12}$ **f.** $y = \frac{10}{3} - \frac{2}{3}x$

2. The equations for the lines are:

   L1: $y = 5 - \frac{5}{12}x$ L2: $y = 6 - x$

   L3: $y = \frac{4}{5}x + \frac{12}{5}$ L4: $y = \frac{1}{4}x - 10$

3. **a.** $C = 2.1n + 1.15$

   b. 1.15; This is the cost for shoe rental.

   c. 2.1; This is the cost of bowling each game.

   d. $13.75

   e. Tony bowled 3 games.

coefficient A number that is multiplied by a variable in an equation or expression. In a linear equation of the form $y = mx + b$, the coefficient, m, of x is the slope of the graph of the line. For example, in the equation $y = 3x + 5$, the coefficient of x is 3. This is also the slope of the line.

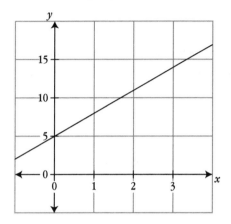

constant term A number in an equation that is not multiplied by a variable—an amount added to or subtracted from the terms involving variables. In an equation of the form $y = mx + b$, the y-intercept, b, is a constant term. The effect of the constant on a graph is to raise or lower the graph. The constant term in the equation $y = 3x + 5$ is 5. The graph of $y = 3x$ is raised vertically 5 units to give the graph of $y = 3x + 5$.

coordinate pair A pair of numbers of the form (x, y) that gives the location of a point in the coordinate plane. The x term gives the distance left or right from the origin $(0, 0)$, and the y term gives the distance up or down from the origin.

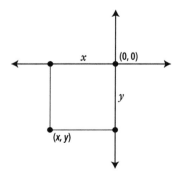

function A relationship (usually) between two variables. A relationship is a function if there is only one value of the second variable for each value of the first variable. For example, distance depends on, or is a function of, time: the distance traveled depends on the time. The performance of a person running 5 mph can be represented by the equation $d = 5t$, where d is distance in miles and t is time in hours. This function is a linear function whose graph is a straight line with a slope of 5. If the cost of buying T-shirts is $100 plus $7 per shirt, the total cost depends on the number of T-shirts bought and is a linear function represented by the equation $C = 100 + 7n$, where C is the total cost in dollars and n is the number of T-shirts. Other functions are not linear. For example, the equation for the area of a square is $A = s^2$, where s is the length of a side.

linear relationship A relationship in which there is a constant rate of change between two variables; for each unit increase in one variable, there is a constant change in the other variable. A linear relationship between two variables can be represented by a straight-line graph and by an equation of the form $y = mx + b$. The rate of change is the coefficient, m, of x. (Sometimes the word *linear* is used to describe any relationship, function, or pattern that can be represented by a straight-line graph.) For example, if you save $2 each month, the amount you will have saved at the end of 12 months is $24, which can be computed by the equation $y = 2x$. The constant rate of change is 2.

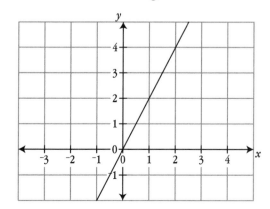

origin The point where the x- and y-axes intersect on a coordinate graph. With coordinates (0, 0), the origin is the center of the coordinate plane.

point of intersection The point where two graphs cross. We are usually interested in the coordinates of this point because those x and y values are solutions to both equations. The graphs of the equations $y = x$ and $y = 2x - 3$ intersect at the point (3, 3). This number pair is a solution to each equation.

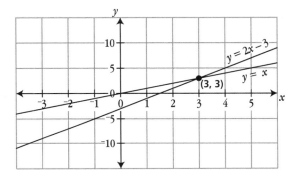

rise The vertical change between two points. When calculating the slope of a line, the rise is the numerator in the ratio.

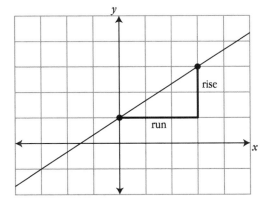

run The horizontal change between two points. When calculating the slope of a line, the run is the denominator in the ratio.

scale Determines the distance between and the label for tick marks on the x- and y-axes of a coordinate grid. When graphing—with either a graphing calculator or using paper and pencil—an appropriate scale must be selected so that the resulting graph is helpful. For example, when graphing the equation $d = 60t$ (or $y = 60x$), it would not be reasonable or efficient to select a scale of 1 for both the x- and y-axes. A graphing calculator screen is not large enough to properly display the graph of this equation with this scale, and a scale of 1 is not an efficient choice for making a graph by hand. In both cases, a scale of 1 for the x-axis and a scale of 15 or 30 for the y-axis would be more reasonable.

slope The number that relates the steepness of a line. The slope is the ratio of the vertical change to the horizontal change between any two points on the line. Sometimes this ratio is referred to as *the rise over the run*. The slope of a horizontal line is 0. Slopes are positive if the y values increase from left to right on a coordinate grid and negative if the y values decrease from left to right. As a line gets steeper, approaching a vertical line, the slope approaches positive or negative infinity. The slope of a vertical line is undefined.

The slope of a line is the same as the constant rate of change between the two variables. For example, the points (0, 0) and (3, 6) lie on the graph of $y = 2x$. Between these points, the vertical change is 6 and the horizontal change is 3, so the slope is $\frac{6}{3} = 2$, which is the coefficient of x in the equation.

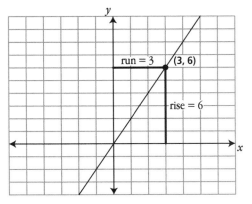

steepness The incline of a line. A line that goes up and to the right has a slope of 1 if it is rising at the same rate as it is moving to the right. An example of such a line is the graph of the equation $y = x$. If a line has a slope greater than 1, we might call it steep. For example, if a line rises 3 units for each 1-unit increase to the right, it has a slope of 3 (such as $y = 3x$). If a line rises 30 units for each 1-unit increase to the right, it has a slope of 30 (such as $y = 30x$) and is even steeper. If the slope is less than 1, the line is not as steep (such as $y = 0.5x$).

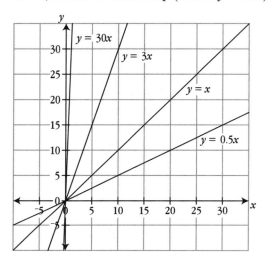

x-intercept The point where a graph crosses the x-axis. (These numbers are also called the *roots* or the *zeros* of the equation; these terms are not used in this unit. A linear equation has only one root, which means it crosses the x-axis only once.) The x-intercept of the equation $y = 3x + 5$ is $(0, -\frac{5}{3})$, or $-\frac{5}{3}$.

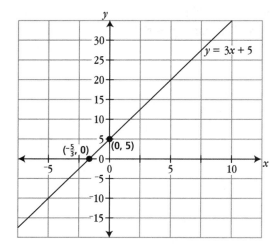

y-intercept The point where the graph crosses the y-axis. This number is the constant, b, in a linear equation of the form $y = mx + b$. In the graph above, the y-intercept is $(0, 5)$, or 5.

Index